# Up to Your Armpits in Alligators?

### How to sort out what risks are worth worrying about!

**JOHN PALING**

with additional material
by Sean Paling

# *Introducing*
# *The Paling Perspective*
# *Scale*<sup>SM</sup>

*A simple tool for*

☞ *Communicating relative risks to the public*

☞ *Prioritizing risks and resources for businesses*

☞ *Helping individuals deal with the confusing blizzard of reported hazards in their lives.*

# Risks and the Law

*Since the main purpose of this work is to offer a new tool for understanding and communicating risks (rather than to report newly calculated risks), the authors and publishers have used other original sources for all the risk assessments incorporated in this book. Any slights to people or organizations or the causes they represent are unintentional.*

*We assume no responsibility for errors, inaccuracies, omissions or any inconsistency herein. Any conclusions that may be drawn from figures in this book should be viewed as tentative and are not intended to serve as advice or guidance for the reader's personal decisions with regard to acceptable risks.*

*The author welcomes exploring with all other parties how this scale may be used to objectively display their account of the levels of risk involved in their particular area of concern.*

First Printing and Copyright © 1994 John Paling and Sean Paling
Revised& Reprinted © 1997 by John Paling

For information contact:
**Risk Communication & Environmental Institute,**
**5822 N.W. 91st Boulevard, Gainesville, Florida 32653.**

ISBN 0-9642236-6-X
1.Risk Communication. 2. Success in Business I. Title.

Printed in the United States of America

# TABLE OF CONTENTS

# *Dedication*

*This book is for those who seek to use this simple scale with integrity and with the goal of putting the minor risks of our lives into an appropriate perspective, thus permitting society to focus first on the most important risks to our communities.*

*We hope that clarifying the realities of life will liberate more people to appreciate the many benefits of our modern lifestyle, yet remain alert to protecting our families from the worst abuses of modern human society on our planet.*

# ABOUT THE AUTHORS

## JOHN PALING, PH.D.

Dr. John Paling was the producer/cameraman of a recent National Geographic Society TV Special that involved swimming literally "up to the armpits" with 12-foot long alligators. The film was awarded two Emmys and illustrated that assessing risk is a crucial ingredient in surviving as a wildlife cameraman!

Since 1968, Dr. Paling has been engaged in popularizing science as a producer and photographer of numerous international television programs. This unique experience as a public communicator lead him to develop his first "Richter Scale for Risks" which has become the basis of this book.

Born in England, he started his teaching career as an associate professor of biology at the University of Oxford in England and later as a Regent's Professor at the University of California at Santa Cruz.

In 1981, he moved to America where initially he impacted the corporate world as a presenter by using his extensive knowledge (and films) of animals to teach the basic principles of "Strength through Balance". In particular he focused on issues of "Succeeding through Change" and "Positive Environmentalism". Currently, he is in demand as a keynote speaker and consultant focusing on "Communicating Relative Risks" and "Putting Life into Perspective".

I

John Paling began studying risk as a result of simply trying to sort out for himself some basis for establishing personal priorities from among all the environmental worries he heard about in the media every day. Initially researching purely for his own sake, he tried out different ways of cutting through many of the complexities that have previously hindered ordinary citizens from getting any understanding of the **relative** risks to their lives.

He sees himself as "simply a member of the general public who is trying to make sense of what the experts can tell us" and wants to share with all non professionals scientifically valid perspectives that we can all use to make better decisions in our lives.

Although Dr. Paling now holds a faculty position at the Center for Environmental & Human Toxicology at the University of Florida, he describes himself as "essentially self-taught" and makes no claims to be a mathematically trained risk assessor. However, he has studied the problem of *effectively communicating risk* in great detail and has great faith in the value of his unique appoach.

In designing "The Paling Perspective Scale$^{SM}$", he has brought to bear his unique ability to understand both the mind set of the general public and the key principles of this rapidly growing science.

Additional material
relating to the safety of nuclear
power generation was provided by

# SEAN PALING

who also served as an invaluable catalyst
for the first edition

Sean Paling is one of John Paling's two sons. He is a research physicist who currently teaches physics and mathematics at the University of Leeds in England. Formerly, he specialized in radiation and measurement techniques for General Electric's Nuclear Medical Research Division in England. His main field of research is now in studies of cosmic rays and astrophysics.

Mr. Paling first became involved in risk communication simply as a family advisor, but with his academic background and training, his contribution has become an important component of the project, most specially in the area of nuclear risks.

Through his work, he has travelled extensively worldwide. His main hobby is the statistically risky pursuit of rock climbing!

*"We offer
a framework that
serves as a giant step
forward in making
relative risk assessments
literally a household
subject."*

*If you are feeling swamped*
*...and you don't know which way to turn...*

*Then here's a way to sort out what's
really worth worrying about!*

# INTRODUCTION

This is the revised and expanded second edition of our little book outlining an exciting work in progress. It introduces the reader to a unique perspective scale for understanding and explaining relative risks. This version has been written to address the huge demand from businesses, health and safety professionals and the media who wish to use this communications tool to help solve problems and prioritize issues in their professional and personal lives.

My own introduction to the disconnection between the level of seriousness of problems and the amount of money we spend on them came in the environmental field as a result of comments from the then Assistant Administrator of the United States EPA, Dr. Charles Grizzle. He had attended one of my presentations on "Positive Environmentalism" and suggested that I consider using my communications skills to help get the message out that society should take more account of the relative seriousness of the many risks to our lives when we try to find a balance between economic and environmental priorities.

That conversation played on my own long-standing concern to be better aware personally of what really mattered most among the deluge of environmental problems that were being unearthed at the time. It also crystallized an incident that had been troubling me for more than five years.

I never had a good answer for a woman who stopped me in the lobby of a conference center. She was taking a cigarette break and asked me, "Do you really think it's worthwhile buying a water purification system for my house so I will know that the water really is safe?" It never occurred to me to point out that, while it is appropriate for everyone to thoroughly check out whatever might concern us, she was focusing a huge amount of energy on a relatively small risk while ignoring a much larger one.

From that moment on, I was alerted to the need for a simple "Richter Scale for Risks." I found that ordinary people everywhere were desperate to get a better handle on the innumerable risks to their family's lives that constantly cry out to us from the media. They had a deep-seated distrust of businesses yet industrial operations and products were usually the main source of their worries.

In the absence of a simple tool that puts risks in perspective in a consistent framework, citizens were usually skeptical, and often scared. They had no way of knowing how much they should worry about the emissions from the local chemical company, pesticide residues on food, or electrical fields from power lines. The average person was alarmed yet totally confused when it came to deciding how to react to the current "worry of the week" or "molecule of the month".

I soon found that the frustrations of citizens were matched by the despair of corporations, particularly those in the manufacturing and insurance industries.

Corporate communicators have been conspicuously unsuccessful in getting the public to understand the truth about the relatively minute level of risks that many of their business activities actually represent. But instead of continuing to focus on ways to communicate what really matters most – namely how serious is the *real* hazard – they have been persuaded to concentrate instead only on those factors that influence the public's outrage over what is *perceived* as a major risk.

The encouraging, positive feedback from the first book gives us the confidence to challenge businesses who doubt that *facts* can ever be communicated successfully when issues of risk are so often loaded with *emotion*. A neutral perspective scale that makes sense to everyone can help reassure a community by honestly discussing relative risks and moving discussions away from purely anecdotal experiences.

**For corporate communicators,** this is a tool to help put concerns about industrial activities into perspective for communities and the media by expressing them in a context of relative risks.

**For management,** this framework can show and prioritize the real Risk Factors that threaten ongoing business success. This empowers executives to make better decisions in apportioning resources so that they provide most value and strength to their organizations.

**For professionals in health and safety, the media and civil and social rights issues**, this scale is a fresh, new way to reach out to those who previously have never seemed to understand or respond to your message.

**For society,** this framework holds out the major benefit of making comparative risk assessment <u>literally</u> a household subject in a similar way to predictions of the weather. This has far reaching implications on how we will all discuss and decide on the major issues of the 21st century.

We continue to develop new versions of our scale focusing on different aspects of life. As part of this process, we have been putting other societal and medical issues in perspective alongside the other risks of the average citizen's life. These topics will be the focus of our next book which will be targeted specifically for the general public.

Hopefully, this edition will help business readers by showing that many of the "alligators" that seem to float around will be less threatening now that there is a way of putting them into perspective and prioritizing them with Risk Factors. Just as important, we hope that by positively facing realities, appreciating the many benefits of our contemporary lives and not despairing as a result of exaggerated fears, we will help all individuals who have ever felt that they are **Up to Their Armpits in Alligators!**

We put this framework in the hands of the reader with the request that the copyright limitations on this intellectual product be respected. We welcome active collaborations with interested professionals in other fields and we encourage people to use the scale but ask that its origins be appropriately acknowledged.

Take Care & Enjoy!

*John Paling*

Gainesville, Florida
August 20th, 1996

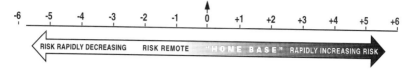
# - 1 -

# THE PROBLEM:
## What's worth worrying about in life?

In recent years, the public has been overwhelmed by the growing number of news reports announcing different issues that seem to threaten our daily lives. Until now, citizens, the media and legislators have had no simple way of sorting out the relative importance of new risks and putting them into perspective alongside other societal, environmental and public health hazards. What we are offering here is an effective communications tool that helps people make sense out of all these worries.

The continued absence of such a "Richter Scale for Risks" has led to a string of undesirable consequences that extend from economic extravagance to public paranoia. Among the problems:

✖ Businesses are often burdened with expensive and time consuming regulations that may not even improve the public health yet certainly cost jobs

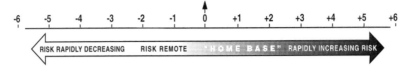

and cause the migration of existing businesses from communities. For this reason, a case is now being made in the Congress of the United States that future regulatory demands should take into account comparisons of relative risk assessments and not be driven predominately by public panic.

✖ At present, pollution prevention expenditures are often allocated more according to the level of the society's worries than to what experts calculate are the greatest real risks. Common sense dictates that we should all focus our environmental protection efforts to achieve the greatest risk reduction first.

✖ Legislators and politicians are often frustrated because there is no simply understood way to prioritize our major public health concerns so that society can see the sense of channeling its efforts toward combatting the major concerns first.

✖ The public urgently seeks some perspective to sort out what the relative levels of risk are for different reported hazards. Only then can individuals make better choices about those risks that affect their lives and those of their families. At

THE PALING PERSPECTIVE SCALE

the same time, they should be reassured by what most professional toxicologists see as genuinely trivial risks and the fact that there are many levels of safety already built into our regulations.

✖ Citizens are weary of the constant deluge of environmental and health alarms which are typically presented as if they are all equally serious. In the early 1990s, the continuing stream of reports of environmental risks finally weakened the public's enthusiasm to undertake fresh initiatives while there never seemed to be any real progress on solving those worries that were already clouding the public's mind.

✖ The general public cannot easily understand the work of professional risk assessors in part because different types of risks are expressed in different and confusing scientific units.

✖ The media have had no simple, consistent and universal communications tool to plot and discuss relative risks in their reports.

✖ Different government agencies have different definitions of "safety" and no one has the overall responsibility of communicating to the public about the *relative* risks of different hazards to their lives.

*"This one simple scale can be used to express the position of every different type of risk that may affect anyone on earth!"*

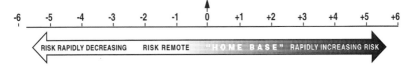

THE PALING PERSPECTIVE SCALE

RISK RAPIDLY DECREASING    RISK REMOTE    RAPIDLY INCREASING RISK

# - 2 -

# THE SOLUTION:
## Looking at risks in perspective

We have developed a new, objective comparative scale that reflects the relative levels of risk from different hazards in a manner that is readily understood by the public, the media and legislators, yet which is based on sound risk assessment practices. Please refer to Fig.1 (page 6) for the basic scale matrix.

**It is no exaggeration to say that this one simple communications tool can be used to express the position of every different type of risk that may affect anyone on earth!**

If someone has done a risk assessment calculation and claims to have figures showing the levels of risk for a particular hazard under certain circumstances, then this scale can show it. It answers the general public's wish to be able to cut through all the technical stuff and get a simple answer to the question "What's the bottom line for this particular risk?"

-6  -5  -4  -3  -2  -1 EFFECTIVE 0 ZERO  +1  +2  +3  +4  +5  +6

# FIG. 1 THE PALING PERSPECTIVE SCALE℠

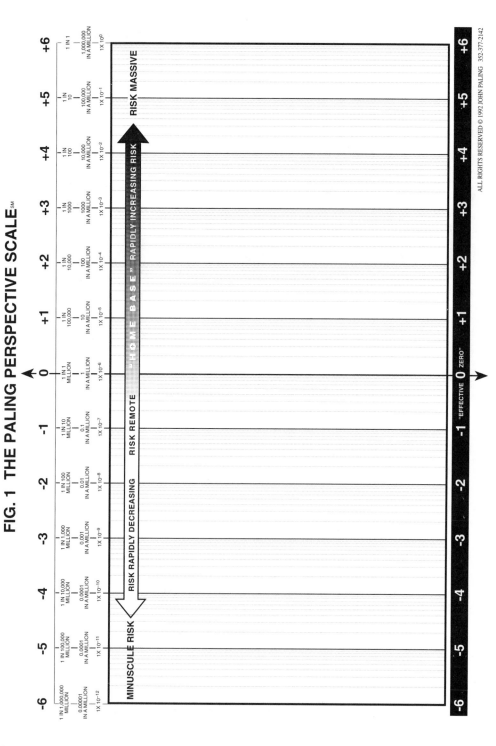

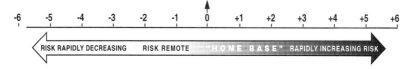

Our scale gives them precisely that. It starkly shows along the "bottom line" simple numbers for all the levels of risk that could ever be important to the life of any individual on the planet. The scale ranges from a "-6" through "Zero" to "+6," and effectively every single risk that we know of can be positioned on this one scale!

When you follow each of these numbers upwards to the top of the chart, the same levels of risk are expressed in three different ways. In other words, (starting upwards from the right hand bottom corner) a bottom line figure of a "+6" on our scale is the same as a risk of 1 in 1, which is the same thing as a risk of 1,000,000 in a million; and that is the same as what mathematical types call a risk of $1 \times 10^0$.

Similarly, our bottom line risk level of a "+2" is the same as an estimated risk of 1 in 10,000, which is the same as a risk of 100 in a million, and that in mathematical jargon is the same as a risk of $1 \times 10^{-4}$.

Figures in the "minus" zones to the left of center become rapidly less risky or less likely to occur, while those in the "plus" zones to the right of center become rapidly more serious in the sense that they are more likely to occur.

*Simply put, The Paling Perspective Scale*ᔆᴹ *is a versatile communications tool that:*

✓ Allows the recording of all calculable risks on a scale of "-6" to "+6," with zero being perceived, for all practical purposes, as totally safe for the vast majority of people on the planet.

✓ Identifies its Zero point based on levels of risk that the public knowingly recognizes, yet chooses to ignore by not changing existing behaviors materially. (We demonstrate later that our Zero point is about 10 to 100 times LESS risky than most risks that the public is totally "at home" with. In other words, if anything, it is over protective of the public's interests.)

✓ Compares many different types of risks by expressing them all as chances in a million - immaterial of the original chemical/nuclear/ electromagnetic or medical units in which the concentrations and risks were initially measured.

✓ Enables communicators to show the relative levels of risk associated with different hazards against a bottom line number that the public easily becomes intuitively familiar with. (In the same way that most Americans have come to understand the relative size of an earthquake by hearing a single figure on the Richter Scale, yet they have no idea of how that scale works.)

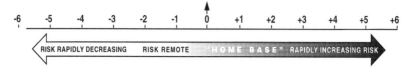

✓ Serves as a platform for risk assessment professionals to communicate with the public on the relative odds of potential hazards under different circumstances (including expression of estimates of uncertainty).

✓ Has very wide applications. In particular, it provides an effective new way for industries to communicate environmental, health and safety risks to the public. It is also valuable for comparing the media's newly discovered "worry of the week" with routine societal risks.

✓ Empowers non-technical citizens by enabling them to better understand and compare the odds of different risks for themselves.

✓ Is a major improvement on the many negative situations listed in Chapter. 1.

In evaluating most things in life, everything comes down to a matter of balance. Our scale does have its limitations (some of which are discussed later in Chapter 9). However, we sincerely believe that these are vastly outweighed by the benefits the scale offers us all by providing a clearer sense of the *relative* levels of risks for many of the important concerns in our lives.

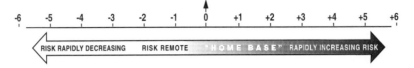

THE PALING PERSPECTIVE SCALE

-6  -5  -4  -3  -2  -1  0  +1  +2  +3  +4  +5  +6

RISK RAPIDLY DECREASING    RISK REMOTE    HOME BASE    RAPIDLY INCREASING RISK

## Forces Promoting the Acceptance of the Scale

There are many reasons why we are optimistic that the present framework will gain widespread acceptance as a valuable communications tool.

First, all our discussions and presentations over the past few years have demonstrated an overwhelming enthusiasm for the scale and its applications. People from all backgrounds relate to its simple conceptual basis and are almost elated to see our first step toward some logical and visual apportionment of relative risks. The scale holds great promise to answer the needs of a wide range of organizations and individuals who have experienced the frustrations from the present stream of unquantified claims of public health hazards.

Secondly, there is a widespread feeling among risk professionals in the United States that there is a need to reassure the public about the relative safety of our modern lifestyle, not least evidenced by our ever increasing average lifespan. Since the equipment that we use to detect chemicals has become more and more sensitive over recent years, we can now detect such infinitely minute quantities of pollutants that it has become clear that just

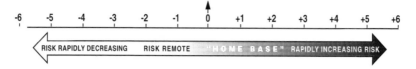

THE PALING PERSPECTIVE SCALE

about everything contains "toxic chemicals" at some level or another! (In U.S.A., the familiar initials of the Environmental Protection Agency "EPA" are sometimes jokingly switched to "Everything Pollutes Anyway!")

The truth is that we are *all* exposed to "cancer causing" chemicals. But, most importantly, many of them have nothing to do with industrial activities.

Indeed, we now recognize that plants naturally produce all manners of poisons as a defense against the many animals and fungi that would otherwise wipe them out. In other words, our regulations have to come to terms with the fact that totally healthy fruits and vegetables often contain minute quantities of natural poisons that, if they were produced by industry, would be banned as unsafe! Clearly, this awareness (expertly demonstrated by Dr. Bruce Ames of University of California, Berkeley and others) must lead to a rethinking of what we all mean by "risky."

We are surrounded by a world of hundreds of potential, but infinitesimal, chemical hazards. *The dose alone determines whether or not you are dealing with a poison.* For the vast majority of our life's experiences, minute doses are simply not poisonous.

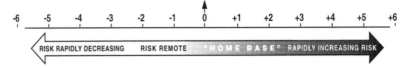

THE PALING PERSPECTIVE SCALE

We believe that only by showing some measure of the *relative* risks involved can communicators help society be better informed about how much concern should be devoted to any particular alarm.

Encouraged by the fact that the public can easily understand and intuitively accept a visual display of different risks on perspective scale, we particularly hope that the media will choose to report estimates of new risks in a relative context.

Further urgency for such a prioritized scale in the U.S. comes from the decision to make the military subject to the same environmental laws as the rest of the country. This is likely to incur considerable costs, and this money of course will have to come from tax payers. Already this additional financial burden is being challenged by the Pentagon as requiring clean-up at levels that are too costly for the small benefits involved.

Environmentalists too are increasingly aware that some cost-benefit studies are needed to best spend the available clean-up dollars. Thus, on all sides, involved parties are recognizing that, ideally, a measure of comparative risk assessment should be incorporated as an integral part of decisions on such clean-up processes.

Finally, much though purists will bemoan it, we have found that the public is desperate to have use of an all embracing, "USA Today-style" scale - such as ours. Given the enormous information overload that is common to our modern lifestyle, people have little time to sort through and try to understand all the various current methods of trying to compare risks.

*With our scale, relative levels of risk quickly become intuitive, based on a simple number between "zero" and "+6." This offers an irresistible improvement on anything else out there and it moves us all towards the much sought after goal of simplification of expression, yet it is still based upon available published science.*

William Reilly, a widely respected former administrator of the EPA, clearly made the case for adopting a better tool to effectively communicate relative risks. He summarized the main benefit in these persuasive terms:

**"Using risk as a common denominator creates a measurement that lets us distinguish between the environmental equivalents of heart attacks from indigestion, and broken bones from bruises."**

*"It should no longer be a news story that someone is exposed to toxic or cancer-causing chemicals."*

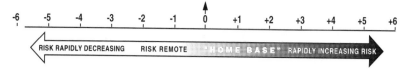

# - 3 -

# THE CONCEPTUAL BASIS FOR "THE PALING PERSPECTIVE SCALE^SM"

Like all good ideas, the basis of our scale is very simple. Indeed, all the basic concepts behind it already exist. What we believe that is distinctive and important is how we put them together.

We begin by recognizing that *everything* we do in life has some risk associated with it. For example, just staying in your own home for your (70-year) lifetime holds 7,700 chances in a million of you incurring a fatal accident! From the moment you wake up to your morning cup of coffee (cancer risk from dioxin in the bleached coffee filter) to the time you finally retire under your electric blanket at night (possible harmful effects of electromagnetic forces), your life is in danger. And staying in bed every day would give you some calculable risk of developing bed sores! Even distilled water will kill you - if you drink 15 gallons a day!

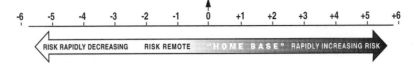

This is not said to taunt my many friends who are environmentalists but to make us all face the reality that, at some level, all life incurs risks and we have to see public health and environmental risks in some perspective if we are to make sense of them.

**The undeniable truth is that there is really no such thing as "zero risk!" This should be the first rule for understanding risk assessment! We all live lives that have all sorts of remote chances of disaster happening to us,** *yet most people accept these risks as effectively inconsequential and do not feel they need to take any exceptional precautions or alter their behavior to avoid them.*

## Home Base and Effective Zero

So, for the primary concept of our scale, we started by looking at risks that intuitively "mean something" to the public. We identified risks that people are "at home" with, in both senses of those words. We looked to see what people take for granted when they feel something is, as the British say, "safe as houses." How serious are the normal *domestic* risks in or around the home that homeowners are comfortable (at home) in accepting

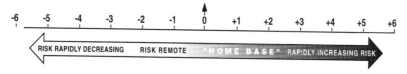

## THE PALING PERSPECTIVE SCALE

-6  -5  -4  -3  -2  -1  0  +1  +2  +3  +4  +5  +6

RISK RAPIDLY DECREASING    RISK REMOTE    "HOME BASE"  RAPIDLY INCREASING RISK

and view as, relatively speaking, not worth bothering about, based on their real life experiences!

(Naturally, avoiding hazards assumes that the householder exercises the common sense precautions that we all learn growing up. For example, normal people don't deliberately throw themselves head first down the stairs or poke their fingers into a live power circuit!)

We researched the literature and have listed the odds quoted for some of these real risks associated with daily life that most people ignore and hence fall into our "Home Base" range. (*Our sources for all the points in the charts throughout this book are provided as an addendum.*)

Fig. 2 (page 18) charts some "Home Base" risks.

It can be seen that some of these serious risks carry the odds of occurring no more than one chance in 10,000 (E.g., risk of death from accidents at home in one year; risk of being struck by lightning in the U.S.; risk of mother dying in birth of a single child). Others carry one chance in a 100,000 (E.g., several common foods and drinks at moderate intakes).

-6  -5  -4  -3  -2  -1 EFFECTIVE 0 ZERO  +1  +2  +3  +4  +5  +6

# FIG. 2  RISKS WITH WHICH WE ARE "AT HOME"

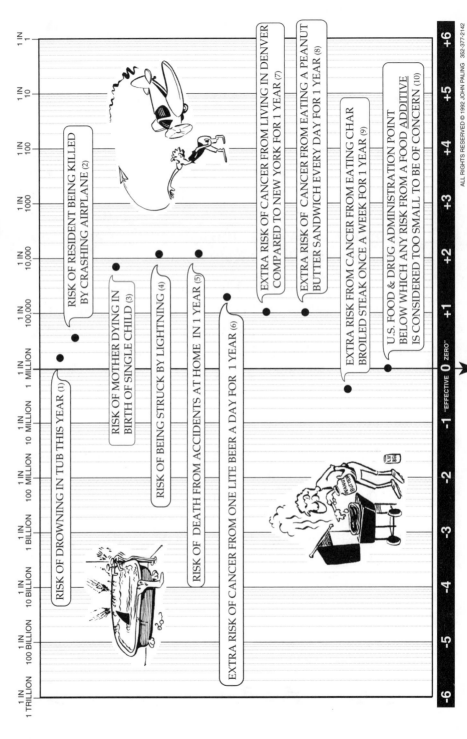

RISK OF DROWNING IN TUB THIS YEAR (1)

RISK OF RESIDENT BEING KILLED BY CRASHING AIRPLANE (2)

RISK OF MOTHER DYING IN BIRTH OF SINGLE CHILD (3)

RISK OF BEING STRUCK BY LIGHTNING (4)

RISK OF DEATH FROM ACCIDENTS AT HOME IN 1 YEAR (5)

EXTRA RISK OF CANCER FROM ONE LITE BEER A DAY FOR 1 YEAR (6)

EXTRA RISK OF CANCER FROM LIVING IN DENVER COMPARED TO NEW YORK FOR 1 YEAR (7)

EXTRA RISK OF CANCER FROM EATING A PEANUT BUTTER SANDWICH EVERY DAY FOR 1 YEAR (8)

EXTRA RISK FROM CANCER FROM EATING CHAR BROILED STEAK ONCE A WEEK FOR 1 YEAR (9)

U.S. FOOD & DRUG ADMINISTRATION POINT BELOW WHICH ANY RISK FROM A FOOD ADDITIVE IS CONSIDERED TOO SMALL TO BE OF CONCERN (10)

| 1 IN 1 TRILLION | 1 IN 100 BILLION | 1 IN 10 BILLION | 1 IN 1 BILLION | 1 IN 100 MILLION | 1 IN 10 MILLION | 1 IN 1 MILLION | 1 IN 100,000 | 1 IN 10,000 | 1 IN 1000 | 1 IN 100 | 1 IN 10 | 1 IN 1 |
|---|---|---|---|---|---|---|---|---|---|---|---|---|
| -6 | -5 | -4 | -3 | -2 | -1 "EFFECTIVE" | 0 ZERO" | +1 | +2 | +3 | +4 | +5 | +6 |

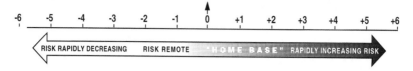

THE PALING PERSPECTIVE SCALE

Other very, very, very remote risks that may be encountered at home (like drowning in the tub this year) are even less likely and are calculated to occur at odds of 10 times less than that, namely around one in a million.

Already the reader begins to get an intuitive feel for how risky a bottom line level of a "+2" or a "zero" is on the scale.

We refer to the area representing risks with odds between one in a million and about one in 10,000 as the "Home Base Zone." (These words appear in white in the appropriate position along the long arrow at the top of our basic scale in Fig. 1, page 6) When translated into the bottom line risk levels of our scale, "Home Base" for fatalities and very serious injuries at home turns out to be between "0" and around "+2."

To add further perspective to the concept of "Home Base" risks, we have included Fig. 3 (page 20). This figure shows the annual risks of having to go to the emergency room of a hospital with injuries "associated with" (not necessarily caused by) different consumer products. These are usually not life threatening, but as might be expected, occur more frequently and hence show up between "+2" and "+ 3¾" on our scale.

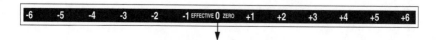

# FIG. 3 RISK OF INJURIES AT HOME

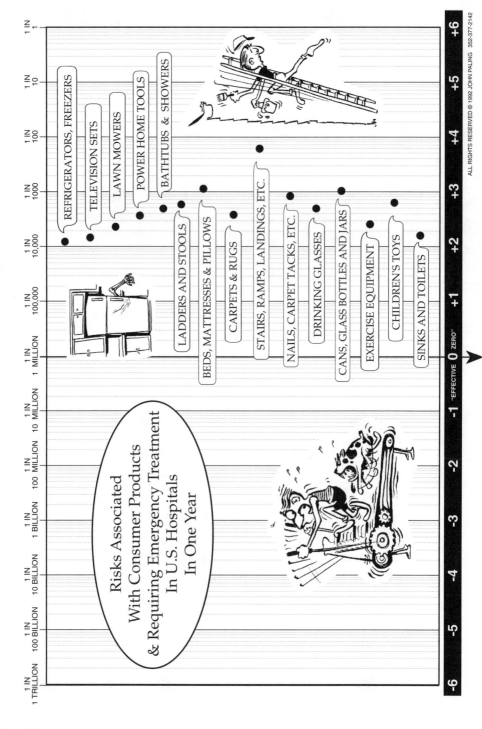

Risks Associated
With Consumer Products
& Requiring Emergency Treatment
In U.S. Hospitals
In One Year

REFRIGERATORS, FREEZERS
TELEVISION SETS
LAWN MOWERS
POWER HOME TOOLS
BATHTUBS & SHOWERS
LADDERS AND STOOLS
BEDS, MATTRESSES & PILLOWS
CARPETS & RUGS
STAIRS, RAMPS, LANDINGS, ETC.
NAILS, CARPET TACKS, ETC.
DRINKING GLASSES
CANS, GLASS BOTTLES AND JARS
EXERCISE EQUIPMENT
CHILDREN'S TOYS
SINKS AND TOILETS

1 IN 1 — 1 IN 10 — 1 IN 100 — 1 IN 1000 — 1 IN 10,000 — 1 IN 100,000 — 1 IN 1 MILLION — 1 IN 10 MILLION — 1 IN 100 MILLION — 1 IN 1 BILLION — 1 IN 10 BILLION — 1 IN 100 BILLION — 1 IN 1 TRILLION

+6  +5  +4  +3  +2  +1  0 ZERO  -1 "EFFECTIVE"  -2  -3  -4  -5  -6

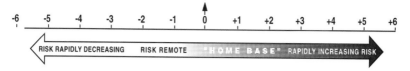

## Minimizing the Risk of Being Misunderstood

Our experience of using the scale with the general public has been very positive. After brief explanations, they readily accept the reality that we are all living with risks in the "0" to "+2" levels in the normal course of our lives. We should certainly be aware of these risks, but most people would not bother altering their lives around because of them.

We have found that, just by examining charts like Fig. 3 on page 20, even the most skeptical soon realize that there is really no such thing as a risk-free life. From our caveman ancestors facing the hazards of nature to our present generation facing the risks of our industrial society, we live through hundreds of risks every day. The crucial difference, however, is that we now survive about three times longer.

It is important to note that the bottom line number on the chart reflects ONLY the likely odds of the particular event that is listed in the relevant balloon. A higher "plus" figure does not necessarily mean something is more serious - just that the risk as stated is *more likely to occur*. For example, the risk of catching a cold this year might be a "+5" on our scale, whereas the risk of dying in an earthquake might be a "+2." Clearly, in this case the more serious risk has the smaller number.

# FIG. 4  A GENERAL PERSPECTIVE SCALE

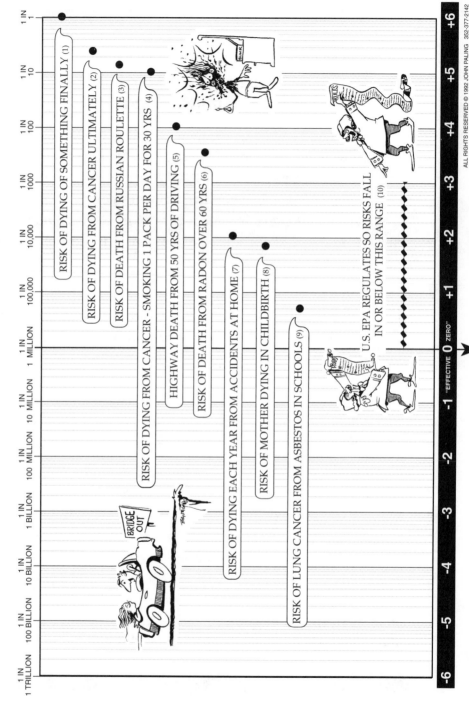

RISK OF DYING OF SOMETHING FINALLY (1)

RISK OF DYING FROM CANCER ULTIMATELY (2)

RISK OF DEATH FROM RUSSIAN ROULETTE (3)

RISK OF DYING FROM CANCER - SMOKING 1 PACK PER DAY FOR 30 YRS (4)

HIGHWAY DEATH FROM 50 YRS OF DRIVING (5)

RISK OF DEATH FROM RADON OVER 60 YRS (6)

RISK OF DYING EACH YEAR FROM ACCIDENTS AT HOME (7)

RISK OF MOTHER DYING IN CHILDBIRTH (8)

RISK OF LUNG CANCER FROM ASBESTOS IN SCHOOLS (9)

U.S. EPA REGULATES SO RISKS FALL IN OR BELOW THIS RANGE (10)

1 IN 1 | 1 IN 10 | 1 IN 100 | 1 IN 1000 | 1 IN 10,000 | 1 IN 100,000 | 1 IN 1 MILLION | 1 IN 10 MILLION | 1 IN 100 MILLION | 1 IN 1 BILLION | 1 IN 10 BILLION | 1 IN 100 BILLION | 1 IN 1 TRILLION

+6 +5 +4 +3 +2 +1 0 "ZERO" -1 "EFFECTIVE" -2 -3 -4 -5 -6

BRIDGE OUT

The *seriousness* of a risk on this simple version of the scale is indicated by the description in the balloon (E.g., "risk of catching a cold"), whereas the likely *probability or odds* of the event is shown by the bottom line number. (E.g., a "+5").

The most important issues stand out when the description in brackets describes a serious category of risk *and* it occurs with a high bottom line number.

**To be on the overly cautious side, we have taken the figure of one in a million as being our "Effective Zero" point for levels of risk.**

To further support the appropriateness of our choice of "one in a million" as our "Effective Zero" point, Fig. 2 (page 18) also shows that this same point is chosen by the U.S. Food & Drug Administration as the risk point below which any risk from a food additive is considered too small to be of regulatory concern. Later it will be seen that the U.S. E.PA. allows risks at and below our "Effective Zero" point to continue without imposing penalties.

**The main message to the public and media is that, when compared to the other risks of life, specific risks that fall in the "minus" or "negative" range of our scale are negligible, for all practical purposes, for the vast majority of the population.**

**THE PALING PERSPECTIVE SCALE**

However, risk assessments can only deal with generalities and it is important that each individual remember that probably **"Nothing is completely risk-free."** By the nature of things, there will always be some people who are exceptionally sensitive or vulnerable to a particular hazard even though it has little or no effect on the rest of society (for example, people who are especially sensitive to pollen or bee stings). No scale can substitute for an individual taking the personal responsibility to act upon what they believe are real hazards for them and adopting sensible precautions. But it remains true that the best guide for individual decision making is to look at the relative risks for the population as a whole.

To get an idea of the likelihood of being affected by some new risk, all you need is an understanding of the framework of the scale and what "Home Base" and "Effective Zero" represent. Then risks of all types can be visually compared to "Effective Zero" by being positioned at the appropriate spot on the scale.

The essence of this approach is that all risks that can be calculated by standard procedures can now be related to these reference levels which the public, using its real life experiences, unconsciously puts in perspective by ignoring or at most not being greatly concerned about.

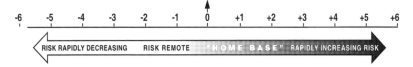

THE PALING PERSPECTIVE SCALE

-6  -5  -4  -3  -2  -1  0  +1  +2  +3  +4  +5  +6

RISK RAPIDLY DECREASING    RISK REMOTE    HOME BASE    RAPIDLY INCREASING RISK

Thus, The Paling Perspective Scale℠ represents a framework that makes it easier for the public to intuitively sense the relative seriousness of reported risks and to quickly recognize that *all worries are not equal.*

Businesses that feel that they are unnecessarily pressured by environmentalists are always asking for a "level playing field." This scale gives them, and everyone else, just that. It has been described as "a football field for society." It is a public communications tool with an easily understood matrix that challenges all parties to establish the relative strengths of their different positions.

**We encourage others to use this scale as a key communications tool to identify *relative risks* and thus provide much needed perspective to the widespread alarm generated by the large number of reported hazards in modern life.**

To allow the public to develop a better feel for risks of different orders of magnitude, we next provide some examples of what sort of risks fall at other points on the scale as well as the "Home Base" areas that we have already identified.

-6  -5  -4  -3  -2  -1 EFFECTIVE 0 ZERO  +1  +2  +3  +4  +5  +6

*"There is
no such thing as
a risk-free lifestyle."*

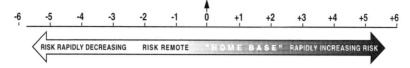

RISK RAPIDLY DECREASING   RISK REMOTE   HOME BASE   RAPIDLY INCREASING RISK

# - 4 -

# A GENERAL PERSPECTIVE SCALE FOR THE UNITED STATES

With an awareness of "Effective Zero" and our "Home Base" concept, the only other preparation needed before we put the scale to work is to establish meaningful examples for all the other important bottom line risk levels on the scale. On the General Perspective Scale in Fig. 4 (page 22), we have added odds for some common experiences which will give members of the North American public a "feeling," a sort of reality check, for the relative significance (and insignificance) of the scale's different bottom line numbers.

In a similar manner, the public now readily accepts the numbers from the Richter Scale for earthquakes. For example, we have come to know that a "5" on the Richter Scale is a fairly large earth tremor that can easily cause damage; that a "3" is fairly common and rarely causes much serious harm; whereas a "7" represents a very serious incident that is likely to cause major devastation.

-6   -5   -4   -3   -2   -1 EFFECTIVE 0 ZERO   +1   +2   +3   +4   +5   +6

Notice that awareness of the Richter Scale numbers is achieved without the public having to know or understand how the calculations or measurements are done. The same is true for our scale.

The current General Perspective Scale (Fig. 4, page 22) provides a mix of annual and lifetime risks that help people get a better feel for the breadth of the scale.

The "Risk of dying of something finally" point is a clear "+6" on our scale. It often amuses people at first sight. However to a risk assessor, it is a valuable reference point because when it comes to *lifetime risks* as opposed to annual risks, we all have to recognize that "something is going to get you in the end." And if you die from something that is a fairly common cause of death, then the aggregated *lifetime risk* for that cause is going to show up on our scale with a high plus figure. (E.g., Cancer from all causes (2), cancer just from smoking (4) and highway deaths (5) in Fig. 4.)

This is a good place to point out that whenever you discuss risks, you have to keep a sharp look out to see whether a particular figure refers to a "lifetime risk" or to an "annual risk." In general, a lifetime risk of something happening would be 70 times

THE PALING PERSPECTIVE SCALE

greater than the risk for a single year - assuming someone is consistently exposed to that particular hazard over a 70-year life span. Since larger levels of risk show up further to the right of our chart, this means that a particular *lifetime risk* is often about one and a half bottom line numbers to the right of the annual risk for the same thing. For this reason, when our scale is used to display different levels of risks for a specific topic, it is best to compare annual levels of risk with other annual risks in order to avoid possibly misleading impressions.

It is instructive to note in Fig. 4 where the average risks for the naturally occurring radiation, radon (6) and asbestos in schools (9), fall on the scale. Radon represents a far higher risk and yet few people recognize and respond to this. This is a prime example of a major disparity between the actual levels of risk they represent in our society and the money spent to combat them. This is the sort of anomaly that this scale will help focus attention on.

In practical terms, each one of us will be more interested in a particular risk as it is likely to affect our circumstances. Thus, the scale could readily be used to show the different points representing the differing level of risks in, say, Florida as opposed

## THE PALING PERSPECTIVE SCALE

-6  -5  -4  -3  -2  -1  0  +1  +2  +3  +4  +5  +6

RISK RAPIDLY DECREASING    RISK REMOTE    HOME BASE    RAPIDLY INCREASING RISK

to Montana; or California as opposed to Maine. Similarly, one version of the chart may show differences in the same risk for different ages, or different races or different careers.

Please remember that all we seek to do in this publication is to demonstrate the need for and the functioning of The Paling Perspective Scale[SM] as a new and effective communications tool for the general public. Once individuals come to intuitively recognize the relative seriousness of risks represented by these bottom line numbers, it is a small step to making sense of any new numbers for other hazards that are put on the scale.

In a short period of time, the public will readily recognize a "-1" risk on our scale as being reasonably ignored, whereas a "+2" risk is approaching something to be taken seriously. Furthermore, a "-4" risk will be seen as something that in other aspects of our lives, we would basically ignore completely. While a "+4" represents a risk so potentially serious that no one should be exposed to it involuntarily without considering all possible options to improve their situation - or at the very least be cautious to know about and minimize the risks involved.

-6  -5  -4  -3  -2  -1 EFFECTIVE 0 ZERO  +1  +2  +3  +4  +5  +6

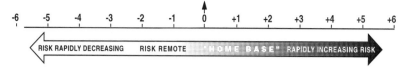

THE PALING PERSPECTIVE SCALE

The basic matrix is intended to be used to locate about a dozen consistent bottom line points that have meaning to members of the general public. Estimates of new risks can be put on the scale and immediately be compared intuitively to known risks for which they already have some level of awareness.

*Since we are using the public's <u>perceptions</u> of different risks as the basis of their intuition for the relative seriousness of different hazards on our scale, we need to take into account what is known about how the public perceives risks. Dr. Peter Sandman, among others, is an excellent professional communicator in this field and defines risk as equalling "hazard + outrage!" Thus, when we select risks to compare, we should strive to find examples that are similar in the public's biases of perception (e.g. all voluntary as opposed to involuntary risks, or all familiar as opposed to unfamiliar, etc.)*

The basic matrix of The Paling Perspective Scale[SM] can be used for any part of the world, with any community and for every possible type of risk (providing only that the estimates can be expressed in terms of so many in a million).

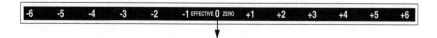

**THE PALING PERSPECTIVE SCALE**

However, specific audiences or geographic areas might benefit from different reference points that are particularly appropriate to the group that the scale is intended to reach. For example, the risk of lightning in Britain is a "0" whereas in the U.S. it is a "+2." Equally the odds of, say, spending a year in prison would be represented by different levels of intuitive risk to different social or economic groups. Also in non-western cultures, local people will bring far more wisdom to choosing appropriate reference points for our main bottom line risk levels than we could ever do.

It is instructive to let everyone develop a basic "Perspective Scale" for themselves so they have a personal background upon which to overlay familiar incidents from everyday life which reflect for them some level of risk. (In our public presentations, attendees are given the opportunity to choose their own examples of risks to match the bottom line numbers for their own version of the Perspective Scale, based upon choices of different statistics that we provide. This is not only entertaining but also produces "ownership" and acceptance of the concepts behind the scale.)

Another preliminary point we should address here is how to deal with different and conflicting figures. One of the side effects of our extensive information technologies is that now we often seem to hear of risk statistics that apparently lead to contradictory conclusions! This may appear to make the selection of figures for the chart more difficult but, instead of getting concerned initially, we recommend putting all reasonable figures on the chart. One of the advantages of this scale is that it visually compresses differences so that often you will find that the zone for a particular risk still makes a valid comparison when related to other zones.

Ideally, all of the figures would be based on the records of government statisticians and professional risk assessors. However, in this preliminary account intended primarily to explain our concept, we have used figures from diverse published sources, some of which are not official authorities. Hence, we draw attention to the disclaimer at the beginning of the book.

*"Every new chemical should not be treated as Pandemonium Chloride"*

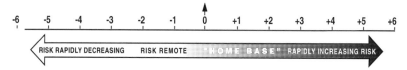

# - 5 -
# THE BIGGEST SECRET IN ASSESSING THE RISKS FROM CHEMICALS

One of the biggest challenges in the last few years is information overload. This applies not just in the area of understanding risks but in every aspect of our lives. There is now so much new information available to each of us that frankly, new facts are ten-a-penny. In contrast, what becomes enormously valuable in this situation are simple new tools for organizing and putting this wide range of facts into perspective. These represent the keys to personal and business wisdom.

The Paling Perspective Scale℠ was developed for exactly this purpose. From the outset, we set out to build a risk communications tool that would give both businesses and the public a way to make sense out of the barrage of worries that we constantly hear about in the media. The outcome is a simple perspective scale that helps deal with the information overload problem by offering a visual way of comparing risks so that they can be understood by ordinary citizens.

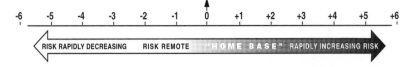

THE PALING PERSPECTIVE SCALE

But some major improvements in the public's willingness to see risks in a different context can come about without using any scale. We have found that a major shift in people's paradigm about pollution risks can arise simply from making them aware of one big change that effectively has been ignored by the media. It is this:

*The main reason we are discovering more and more things to worry about is that the level of sensitivity of our detection equipments has increased dramatically.*

## Why there seems more to worry about!

It has suddenly become evident that virtually every substance, both natural and man-made, contains traces of substances that can be toxic or cause cancer under certain circumstances. Over the past few years, scientists have come up with ultra-sensitive technologies for detecting chemicals in minute quantities.

They can now detect many chemicals at concentrations of one part in a quadrillion. Without some way of visualizing this, it is hard to understand what that represents. It turns out that this is equivalent to being able to detect one second in 32 thousand years. It can also be compared to finding one of these 9" high books in a line of books

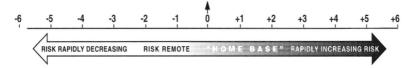

stretching from your hand up to the moon... and back... 300,000 times!

At these levels of sensitivity, it is no wonder that many healthy foods - with or without pesticides - naturally contain quantities of chemicals that, at much larger doses, have been shown to cause diseases in mice or rats. The dose (the amount that actually gets into the body) is one crucial factor in determining whether such minute quantities of a chemical stand a chance of being poisonous.

Responsible reporters already try to provide context to help their readers and listeners understand whether the concentration of some potentially toxic substance even begins to merit public concern. Clearly, every new chemical that surfaces should *not* be treated as "Pandemonium Chloride!"

Even if some substance has been recorded as "causing fatalities" in certain circumstances, it may be totally misleading to report this such that the public gets panicked. Remembering the super-sensitivity of modern detection equipments, a new generation of informed citizens will suspend judgment until they have answers to questions like "How relatively risky do the experts think this new

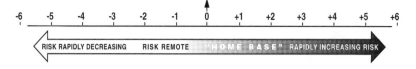

stuff is for real people like me in real life circumstances?" And "How does the level of this new risk compare to all the risks we encounter at home, so that we can use our own experiences of life to assess it for ourselves?"

The best way we know to helpfully answer these questions for the public is to explain the issues in terms of relative risks by using a perspective scale. If this were done for any new concern, it is possible that the potential scare would become insignificant compared to the other risks in our lives.

We believe that many food scares (like the treatment of apples with the chemical Alar which caused a national alarm in the U.S. in 1989) would be viewed with a totally different perspective if the public was already familiar with a comparative risk scale prior to the issue hitting the headlines.

For example, our information shows that the estimated lifetime risk of cancer from Alar was about a +1, while the very worst case figures claimed by activists translate to a +2½ on the chart. (Annual risks would have been about 50 times lower in both cases of course.) If these figures had been reported alongside other lifetime risks that we were all at home with, it is unlikely that citizens would have

## THE PALING PERSPECTIVE SCALE

-6  -5  -4  -3  -2  -1  0  +1  +2  +3  +4  +5  +6

RISK RAPIDLY DECREASING    RISK REMOTE    HOME BASE  RAPIDLY INCREASING RISK

become so hysterical at the time. If the media had adopted a communications tool, like our Richter Scale for Risks, most citizens would have intuitively understood the relative levels of risk that were involved and this would have avoided sparking such an unnecessary level of alarm.

**This calming of excessive public panic is intended as a primary benefit of our perspective scale.**

*(Although the public's perception of the dangers from Alar on apples clearly was greatly exaggerated at the time, there was a separate issue that never received much attention during the scare. Without getting into the whole Alar issue here, a case was also made by environmentalists that the benefits from the use of Alar were all on the side of the industry so any risk to the public, however small, was not merited!)*

For the moment though, let's stick to our most important focus which is to help different groups in society by providing a better understanding of the relative probability of the different risks that we all encounter in our lives.

-6  -5  -4  -3  -2  -1 EFFECTIVE 0 ZERO  +1  +2  +3  +4  +5  +6

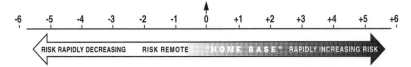

THE PALING PERSPECTIVE SCALE

-6  -5  -4  -3  -2  -1  0  +1  +2  +3  +4  +5  +6

RISK RAPIDLY DECREASING    RISK REMOTE    "HOME BASE"  RAPIDLY INCREASING RISK

*"The fact that something contains cancer-causing substances should not merit a news story!"*

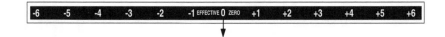

-6    -5    -4    -3    -2    -1 EFFECTIVE 0 ZERO  +1    +2    +3    +4    +5    +6

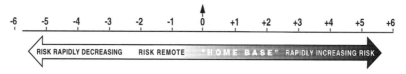

# - 6 -
# PUTTING THE SCALE TO USE

## The Media

*Most immediately, this perspective scale offers the media a tool to display the estimated odds for different risks that become the focus of public attention and to compare them visually to other risks that the public is aware of and therefore can more easily relate to.*

If we are correct in our vision that future reporting will incorporate some estimates of relative risk whenever possible, then we anticipate that both industry and environmental activists will be asked to offer their own account of the level of risk that a particular hazard might cause to exposed individuals and communities.

Initially, one might predict that these estimates will diverge, industry reassuring of low risk and activists claiming high risk! However, if nothing else, that will allow the level of disagreement to be recorded on the scale.

More likely, environmental and health reporters will become aware of the fundamentals of risk assessment and have their own trusted professional advisors and resources so that, as in political

**THE PALING PERSPECTIVE SCALE**

-6  -5  -4  -3  -2  -1  0  +1  +2  +3  +4  +5  +6

RISK RAPIDLY DECREASING    RISK REMOTE    HOME BASE    RAPIDLY INCREASING RISK

disagreements, the editorial commentators will arbitrate a useful middle range.

The job of reporters should be to press the various industry and advocacy groups to back up their concerns (or reassurances) in terms of *levels* of risk such that the public can better make sense of their reports. A key question should always be, "Give me your estimate of how risky you think this is."

Responsible reporters already recognize that **"The fact that something contains cancer-causing substances does not merit a news story!"** Also, if they really want to put their story in context, they will explain how some new risk compares to risks that the public is at home with. And ideally that requires some scale to show relative risks.

## The Public

*We offer the public a simple factual framework to prioritize what their biggest concerns might be and what new information they should have a right to expect when risks are discussed.*

This perspective scale is intended to provide major help to the general public by serving as a platform to display information about the relative levels of risk for issues of concern. We have found that, in a short time, the "bottom line numbers" on

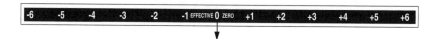

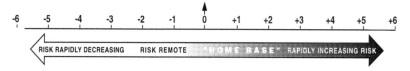

THE PALING PERSPECTIVE SCALE

RISK RAPIDLY DECREASING   RISK REMOTE   HOME BASE   RAPIDLY INCREASING RISK

their own become a shorthand to compare different hazards or the same hazard under different circumstances.

As a starting example, just by responding to Fig. 4, page 22, citizens might agree that it is wise to first check their houses for high levels of radon rather than be concerned initially about risks from asbestos. Equally, if you are a regular smoker (as the woman who first challenged me to consider relative risks was) then you are probably not keeping this in perspective if you are primarily worried about the safety of your water supply.

Later we offer a separate chapter on how the scale can be used by the public to deal with the next risk they hear about.

## Businesses and Industry

*Our scale serves as a valid tool for businesses to show regulators and the public that some costs of clean-up are disproportionate to any possible benefits and that the money might be better spent elsewhere.*

Many changes of attitude and awareness have taken place in the corporate and political world over the past decade. Now most business leaders are deeply concerned about doing what is right for the environment as far as is reasonably practical.

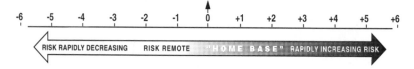

## THE PALING PERSPECTIVE SCALE

RISK RAPIDLY DECREASING  RISK REMOTE  "HOME BASE"  RAPIDLY INCREASING RISK

Just how far some of them would go without pressure is a matter of debate, but it is undoubtedly true that, in general, business leaders genuinely want to be friends of the planet just like everyone else.

To be environmentally responsible often costs businesses more money (and time) than they might have wanted to spend. Yet they are committed to doing whatever it takes, providing they see "a level playing field" and that the rules are unambiguous so they can plan ahead with clarity for what it will take to comply.

Businesses, by nature, are highly sensitive to financial issues. Therefore it irritates many managers to see huge sums being spent on projects that, in their view, provide such insignificant improvements in public health and safety. At the same time, industry can often suggest more meaningful ways that the environment could benefit by the expenditure of that money. Since many business leaders are now pragmatic environmental pioneers, we all might gain by listening closely to the evidence they offer.

The Paling Perspective Scale℠ is clearly a way for the business community to make its point and provide evidence in a form that the public can understand. If a business believes its emissions do not produce serious risks to their communities and

THE PALING PERSPECTIVE SCALE

yet they feel they are over regulated, then an explanation of relative risks is invaluable. With an "Effective Zero" at one in a million and a host of "Home Base" risks in the "+1" and "+2" level, our scale has proved itself to be a useful tool for convincing the general public that industrial risks that fall in the "minus" ranges really are insignificant from any reasonable viewpoint.

## The Medical Profession

*The scale offers a totally new way to assist the medical profession to improve its communications with patients for issues of informed consent.*

One of the most fundamental rights in a democracy is not to be subjected to medical procedures that you do not understand and have not approved. The law requires that each of us give written consent before subjecting ourselves to any surgical procedures. And a crucial element of this process is that first we have been properly informed about the relative risks that we may face.

Most doctors would agree that it is difficult to communicate with patients about the relative risks of possible alternative procedures, let alone to compare these risks with the inevitable other risk- that of doing nothing!

## THE PALING PERSPECTIVE SCALE

This is of massive relevance to the patient of course. But it also has major legal implications for doctors and hospitals. If it turns out that there are problems in surgery or even an unexpected death, then lawyers may be quick to sue if a case can be made that the patient was not properly informed prior to agreeing to the treatment.

We are currently working with physicians who use The Paling Perspective Scale[SM] as a tool for improving the informed consent process for patients and we are interested in pursuing this to the logical conclusion - having the scale used routinely by the medical profession.

## Regulators and Government Agencies

*The scale can provide regulators, government agencies and other organizations with direction as to what is reasonable to spend the most time and money on and a way of explaining their decisions to the public.*

Regulators are well aware that the level of risk alone is not the only criterion that is relevant to making laws for society. Issues like the economic consequences of new legislation, the practical problems of administering the rules and the numbers and circumstances of the people affected all are part of the equation. Also, there are always doubts about how to make rules that deal with small quantities of a chemical that humans may be exposed to over a long period when all we

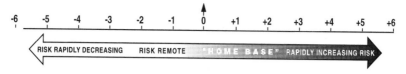

have to go on is what happens when mice are given very large quantities in the lab over a relatively short period.

Then again, the rules that relate to potentially cancer-causing chemicals are different from those that relate to all other substances. Together all these factors make up the difference between "risk assessment" and what is known as "risk management," - that is deciding what levels to allow and what precautions to put in place.

Clearly, the leaders in a democracy are motivated to make regulations that are demanded by the perceptions of their concerned voters. This is why, in our view, it is enormously important that voters be given an easy way of gaining perspective on the levels of risk that different issues represent. If the public comes to expect some evidence of the relative seriousness of the risk, then in the future, totally unprioritized scares might never get out of hand and blown up to unreasonable proportions. This is another way that we see our perspective scale can have immediate benefit.

However, we have learned that with any benefits there usually come risks!

*"The art is to sensibly
balance the risks with
the benefits."*

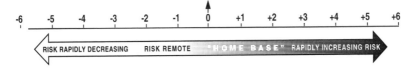

RISK RAPIDLY DECREASING    RISK REMOTE    HOME BASE    RAPIDLY INCREASING RISK

# - 7 -
# BALANCING THE RISKS
# WITH THE BENEFITS - THE
# OTHER HALF OF THE STORY

This chapter introduces two key principles that are almost always involved in the real world of how people deal with risks.

## Some Risks Are Regulated
## More Severely Than Others

The first concerns the fact that there is no single, commonly accepted level of risk that the regulators stick to. For example, the wavy line on Fig. 4, page 22, reflects the range of regulatory upper levels of risks that the EPA allows under different areas of its authority. This often prompts a key question from readers who are just meeting risk assessment issues for the first time: "Why," they ask, "is there such a range of legally allowable levels of risk? You'd think that they would protect the public to the same degree, whatever the risk in question!"

A prime example of this is the chlorination of the public drinking water supply. Undoubtedly, chlorination provides major health benefits in

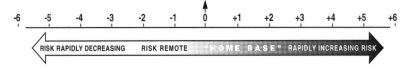

protecting against a wide range of water-borne diseases. However, whenever the domestic water supply is treated with chlorine at the properly prescribed levels, it results in small amounts of nasty chemical by-products in the water that ideally we would rather not have. This side effect is only allowed because there is such a conspicuous balance on the side of the benefits to be gained by the treatment.

So, for regulators as well as citizens, the art is to sensibly balance the risks with the benefits. Sometimes, these benefits are so self-evident that they come to be unconscious (like the convenience of using the car rather than walking for 30 minutes to go the supermarket). At other times, we are conscious that there is a big risk involved so we become extra alert and give special attention to safety while taking advantage of the benefit.

We do this every time we use a potentially dangerous power tool like a chain saw. Unless appropriate care is taken, it is clear that operating a chain saw could lead to a major accident very quickly! Yet the fact that it saves time and sweat over sawing trees by hand makes many rural householders willing to assume the risks, particularly since they feel comfortable about taking care of themselves.

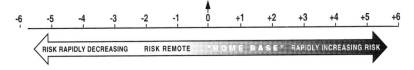

THE PALING PERSPECTIVE SCALE

That brings up the second principle that has huge practical consequences when we start to apply the logic of comparing relative risks. We find that citizens have a much greater tolerance for self-imposed "voluntary risks" than for the same level of risk imposed by others ("involuntary risks").

This difference in our reaction to voluntary as opposed to involuntary risks represents a major issue that is both of practical and ethical concern. Experience shows that rage in society mainly comes from exposure to <u>involuntary risks</u> - particularly those associated with man-made (as opposed to natural) processes and chemicals. This has given rise to the wisecrack in business that citizens want the government to protect them from water pollution so they can live to go hang gliding!

## Perception vs. Reality

This leads us back to the whole area of **perception** of risk as opposed to the estimate of the actual likelihood a particular **hazard** occurring.

Throughout this book, we have been focusing on our tool to communicate the relative level of different hazards but readily acknowledge that issues of perception are of enormous importance

THE PALING PERSPECTIVE SCALE

RISK RAPIDLY DECREASING     RISK REMOTE     RAPIDLY INCREASING RISK

and overriding influence in the public's response to hazards. Indeed, there is truth to the old slogan that "perception *is* reality!"

So powerful are the factors that heighten the public's perception of risks that most researchers and consultants focus on this aspect of communication rather than bringing up the question "How relatively risky is it?" In contrast, while we do not deny the enormous influence of risk perception, we just believe that it is now possible to do a far more effective job of putting risks into context. The public and the media now have a simple, new, factually based comparative scale that lets us all put our worries into perspective. This represents real progress.

We invite others to use our basic chart as a "football field" to record their own risk assessments in a manner that ordinary citizens can easily understand. The more this is done, the more speedily the general public will be able to separate the important from the moderately trivial risks and make choices accordingly.

As the scale becomes a shorthand instrument for recording the relative seriousness of risks in controversial areas, it is to be expected (and in a healthy and desirable way) that the comparative positions on the scale may be attacked by interested parties. For this reason, rather than risk that the whole concept of our scale becoming clouded at the onset by controversies over the location

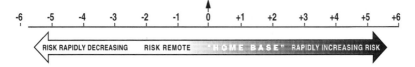

THE PALING PERSPECTIVE SCALE

of particular points, we have deliberately provided relatively few listings in this book. We do not present ourselves here as the primary authorities in the many areas for which the scale has clear applications.

**Therefore, we limit ourselves to using the published figures from others and quoting our sources.** We do not claim to have been exhaustive in unearthing all the publications recording different risk assessments we show on our charts. Instead, in this preliminary publication, we content ourselves with demonstrating the potential of our scale

Understandably, most citizens do not like to hear that a new incinerator, chemical factory or nuclear generator is being proposed in their neighborhood. NOT IN MY BACKYARD! is the predictable reaction. Any discussion about a new industrial operation that may cause pollution brings out all sorts of issues, and the level of the risk involved is always part of the equation. Until now, the public didn't have an intuitive perspective scale to even get a feel for what risks, say, a neighboring nuclear power station would mean to them.

*"If our scale
can make sense
of nuclear risks for
the public, it can handle
pretty well anything!"*

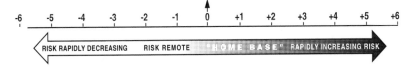

# - 8 -

# PUTTING NUCLEAR POWER INTO PERSPECTIVE

Some readers may see this chapter heading and suddenly fear that what so far has been a nice, easy stroll into the world of relative risks, is about to become heavy going! More than likely, in a million lifetimes, the average citizen would never believe that he or she could ever carry on an informed conversation about nuclear risks with professionals. So with a smile on our scale (page 56), let us face the challenge and use this communication tool to help make sense of what many may start out thinking is an incomprehensible topic.

The science of risk assessment is still in its infancy so we need to remind ourselves that the results of charting risks will always depend on the accuracy of the figures that are used. The best sources for estimates of the different risks will come from the consensus of experts working in the particular area, but also those of their critics.

Here we chose to demonstrate the use of our perspective scale by focusing on one specific area of public concern in England.

# FIG. 5 ANNUAL RISKS ASSOCIATED WITH "SIZEWELL A" NUCLEAR POWER STATION

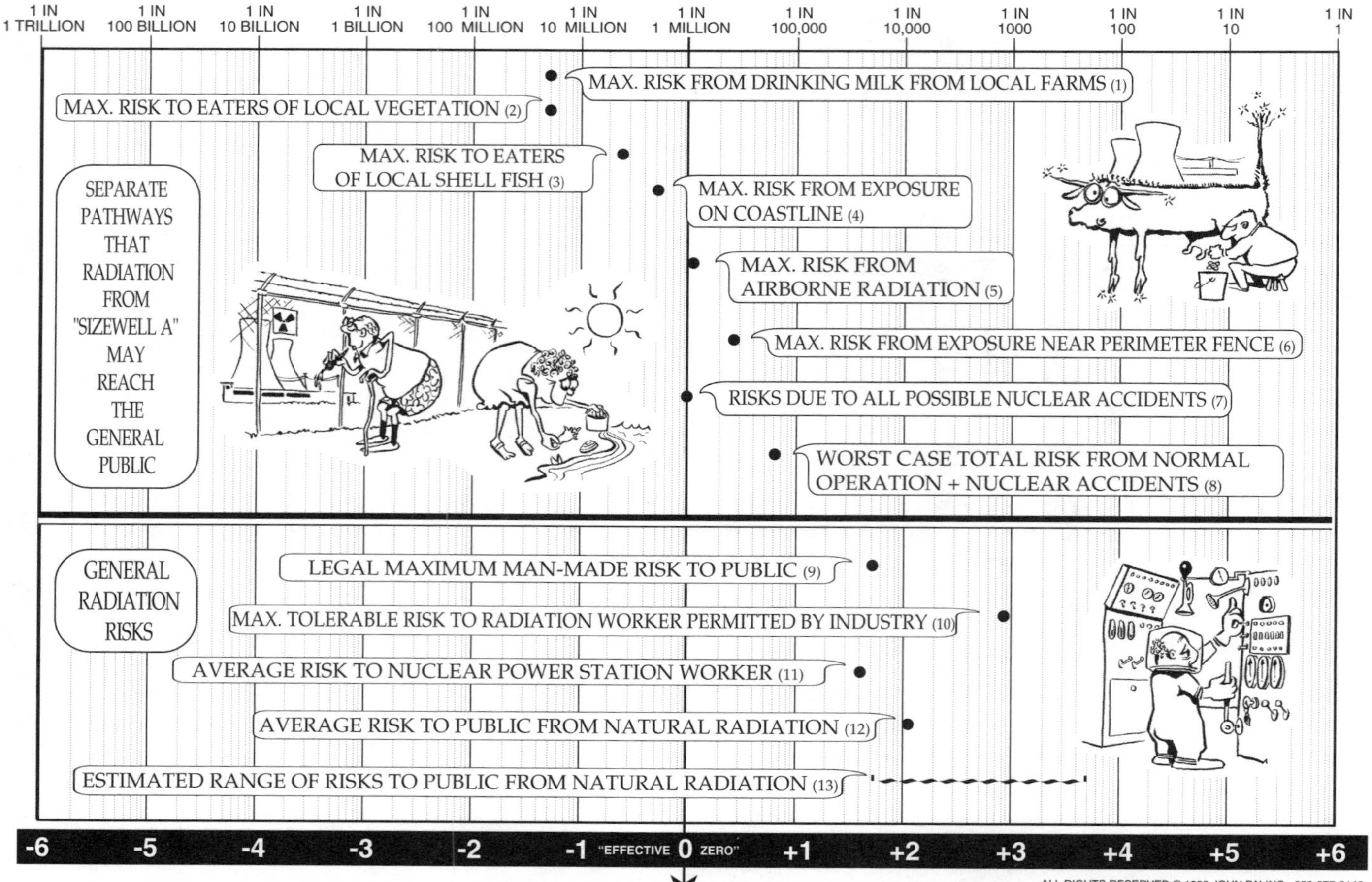

SEPARATE PATHWAYS THAT RADIATION FROM "SIZEWELL A" MAY REACH THE GENERAL PUBLIC

MAX. RISK TO EATERS OF LOCAL VEGETATION (2)

MAX. RISK TO EATERS OF LOCAL SHELL FISH (3)

MAX. RISK FROM DRINKING MILK FROM LOCAL FARMS (1)

MAX. RISK FROM EXPOSURE ON COASTLINE (4)

MAX. RISK FROM AIRBORNE RADIATION (5)

MAX. RISK FROM EXPOSURE NEAR PERIMETER FENCE (6)

RISKS DUE TO ALL POSSIBLE NUCLEAR ACCIDENTS (7)

WORST CASE TOTAL RISK FROM NORMAL OPERATION + NUCLEAR ACCIDENTS (8)

GENERAL RADIATION RISKS

LEGAL MAXIMUM MAN-MADE RISK TO PUBLIC (9)

MAX. TOLERABLE RISK TO RADIATION WORKER PERMITTED BY INDUSTRY (10)

AVERAGE RISK TO NUCLEAR POWER STATION WORKER (11)

AVERAGE RISK TO PUBLIC FROM NATURAL RADIATION (12)

ESTIMATED RANGE OF RISKS TO PUBLIC FROM NATURAL RADIATION (13)

| 1 IN 1 TRILLION | 1 IN 100 BILLION | 1 IN 10 BILLION | 1 IN 1 BILLION | 1 IN 100 MILLION | 1 IN 10 MILLION | 1 IN 1 MILLION | 1 IN 100,000 | 1 IN 10,000 | 1 IN 1000 | 1 IN 100 | 1 IN 10 | 1 IN 1 |
|---|---|---|---|---|---|---|---|---|---|---|---|---|

| -6 | -5 | -4 | -3 | -2 | -1 | 0 ZERO | +1 | +2 | +3 | +4 | +5 | +6 |
|---|---|---|---|---|---|---|---|---|---|---|---|---|
| | | | | | "EFFECTIVE" | | | | | | | |

## Risks to the Public From a Nuclear Power Station

The following account shows how such a highly technical subject as the risks from one particular nuclear power station might be explained simply to society and the media by using The Paling Perspective Scale℠ as the key communications tool. (See Annual Risks associated with Sizewell A Nuclear Power Station Fig. 5 (page 56).

Until now, for a member of the general public to have an intuitive understanding of nuclear risks was about as likely as a layperson attempting brain surgery or the author understanding his own tax forms. (By the way, the risk of being audited by the IRS in the U.S. is about a "+4" on our scale!)

However, we would like to demonstrate that with only a basic knowledge of our scale, an ordinary citizen can easily get a feel for the realities of risks from a nuclear power generator.

*All that is necessary is that the reader is familiar with the concept of "Home Base" risks and the typical levels they fall at on the scale (around and between "Zero" and "+3"). Also, it is important that the reader recognizes that risks begin to get really serious for the population at large at around "+2" and above.*

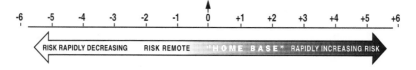

THE PALING PERSPECTIVE SCALE

One of our reasons for choosing this particular issue to demonstrate the use of the scale is because we believe that if our scale can make sense of nuclear risks for the public, it can handle pretty well anything! Also, we are dealing with an industry which has been subject to intense regulation requiring detailed record keeping for many years. Thus, there is an abundance of publicly available risk figures from the nuclear industry.

## How We Got Our Figures

First, because of the strict regulation of nuclear generators, the public should be reassured to know that many technicians sit in the back rooms of nuclear generating plants recording radiation figures in minute detail. However, these figures are not always directly expressed as "levels of risk" so the public normally has no way of assessing their significance.

Currently, the raw figures require some trustworthy translation into "chances in a million" so they can be fitted on to the perspective scale and then can have meaning in the minds of concerned citizens. (The same is true for the raw data for many other areas of risk. Each is measured by professionals

THE PALING PERSPECTIVE SCALE

in its own units and often requires that the initial figures be converted into a measurement that can be positioned on our scale.)

In the case of the Sizewell A nuclear generator in England, we have converted the levels of radiation into levels of risk by making certain assumptions and performing a few calculations to convert the published figures into chances of risk in a million. These figures have been provided to the authorities in charge of safety issues at Nuclear Electric, the parent company of Sizewell A, and they have confirmed their agreement with their accuracy. (More detailed information about the background calculations for these particular points on the scale is included as an addendum to this publication.)

However, Nuclear Electric has not been consulted about our interpretations from the figures and their staff, recognizing this, are understandably concerned that their helpful and open cooperation with us is not seen to be "endorsing our methodology or material." We clearly record their disclaimer. Our wish throughout is simply to show the potential of the scale for improved public communication using their published information.

# How to Make Sense of the Figures

So, with agreement on our recalculations of the figures from the British Nuclear industry, we now invite the reader to use The Paling Perspective Scale℠ to get to a clearer perspective on the significance of various nuclear risks associated with a power station.

First, know that the regulations for the nuclear industry require that every conceivable route by which nuclear radiation might be a hazard to the public should be considered separately and that the MAXIMUM POSSIBLE level of radiation that could come from each particular source is quoted. Thus, in Fig. 5, page 76 you see a point between "-1" and "-2" representing the risk of death from nuclear radiation for the person having the maximum milk consumption from local (radiation contaminated) cows over a year!! (Yes, it really is calculated like that!) On top of that, there is the estimate of radiation consumed in one year by the person who eats the maximum amount of locally grown crops; also recorded as less than a "-1" level.

The listing of these "pathways by which radiation from Sizewell may reach the public" continues with the rest of the possibilities for a person picking up more radiation resulting from the plant. All are recorded at the maximum possible

levels, finishing with the risk from radiation for the person who spends most of his time walking around the perimeter fence of the nuclear generator for a year!

Next, and perhaps least understood by the public, is the figure for the risk of nuclear accidents - a Zero on the scale in Fig. 5. It is a one in a million chance, for that is the level at which engineers are ordered to design and build reactors in Britain and the U.S.

"But what happens if a 747 airplane falls on a nuclear generator?," the skeptic might reasonably ask. The answer is that a power station really is built to withstand even that and still not release dangerous radiations that would cause the public a greater risk than one in a million. If only public communications officers at nuclear generators could get that information out in such a way that it is believed, it might be more reassuring to citizens. But the risks due to all possible nuclear accidents shows as a clear "Effective Zero" on our scale and, unless nuclear opponents have figures to the contrary, then society should be greatly reassured by that aspect of nuclear risk.

Does that mean that nuclear power stations are risk-free? No. Remember, our **first rule of risk assessment is that there is no such thing as zero risk.**

THE PALING PERSPECTIVE SCALE

What it does mean is that compared to other risks (and on the basis of the only figures that we have), it is not serious and there are many other worries that, on levels of risk alone, we should be more concerned about. In fact, when you add up all the risks from the separate sources of nuclear radiation as well as a nuclear catastrophe scenario, the total risk is calculated as less than a "+1" on our scale (Fig. 5, page 56, point 8). In other words, despite all the justifiable concerns as to what can happen without proper regulations (remember Chernoble), Sizewell A Nuclear Power Station is (relatively) very safe indeed.

An important observation to note at the bottom of the scale for "General Radiation Risks." There you see in perspective that, in order to operate by English law, this power station has to operate so that the maximum radiation exposure to the public from all man-made sources and under all probabilities of accidents is about "+1½" - again a very low real risk to the public. Once the reader has developed an intuitive feeling for a "+1" or "+2" level on the scale, we hope that, for the first time perhaps, the general public can put a "+1½" into perspective and sense what this level of risk for nuclear generation represents in an easily understandable way.

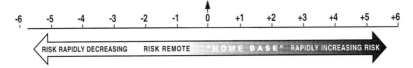

THE PALING PERSPECTIVE SCALE

RISK RAPIDLY DECREASING   RISK REMOTE   HOME BASE   RAPIDLY INCREASING RISK

# Does the Nuclear Industry "Walk its Talk?"

As a result of working on risks for a number of years, we have learned to check if industries really do act on their own reassurances to others. In other words, we have come to question whether those who tell us there is no risk are willing to subject themselves and their families to it!

In the case of the nuclear power generator at Sizewell A, the scale shows that workers in the plant accept maximum levels of nuclear risk far higher than the public would be allowed or expected to tolerate (a "+3" level in fact). Furthermore, the *average* radiation level that a nuclear power station worker receives (point 11) is about the *maximum* level that the public could ever be subjected to - and far higher than the highest calculated risk that the most exposed person would ever receive.

In other words, where these figures fall on the scale reinforces our personal interpretation that the industry does indeed "walk its talk." On the basis of these figures, workers are getting far more radiation than the general public and presumably they value their own safety as highly we would do.

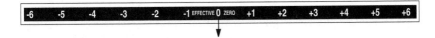

-6  -5  -4  -3  -2  -1 EFFECTIVE 0 ZERO  +1  +2  +3  +4  +5  +6

They obviously find the risks are acceptable when balanced against the alternatives and the economic benefits of the job!!

## Man-made Radiation vs. Natural Radiation

Next, the scale on page 56 introduces another interesting figure to add to our perspective about nuclear risk. Note the wavy line at the bottom. This represents another nuclear risk in England - the risk of dying from *natural* radiation, mainly radon. Radon is a gas that comes up from the ground and is no way related to the nuclear industry.

A line between two points on the scale indicates a range of risks. Depending from which geographic area you measure it, the risk from radon may be as high as a bottom line number of "+3½" but not lower than "+1½" with an average of "+2." Thus, the risk from the worst disaster that has been predicted from the Sizewell A Nuclear Power Station is about ten times LESS than people are already getting from natural radiation from the earth!! This need not mean that radiation from the nuclear plant should be ignored of course, but it certainly provides an illuminating perspective about the realities of the relative risks.

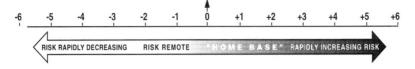

## Another Perspective on Nuclear Risks

All this may suggest to the reader that our bias is "pro-nuclear." But this is certainly not our intention. The above account simply reflects our best attempt to show an honest perspective and interpretation using the scale as a tool for communication and comparisons. We always welcome receiving contrary figures or other interpretations from informed parties.

At present, if one wanted to put the worst light on the published figures from Sizewell A, then you would put "lifetime," as opposed to "annual" risks on to the scale. After all, it is reasonable to argue that citizens may well spend a whole lifetime - not just a year - living on the outskirts of the nuclear generator. When this is done (see Fig. 6, page 66), then the calculated risks do begin to show up on our scale at levels we would recommend as meriting concern . (For this purpose, we have multiplied the annual risk figures by 70 years, an expected lifespan).

On the face of it, we would not feel comfortable living with an average risk of radiation at the "+3¼" level or having a home near the perimeter fence for 70 years and living with a "+2½" risk.

# FIG. 6 LIFETIME RISKS ASSOCIATED WITH "SIZEWELL A" NUCLEAR POWER STATION

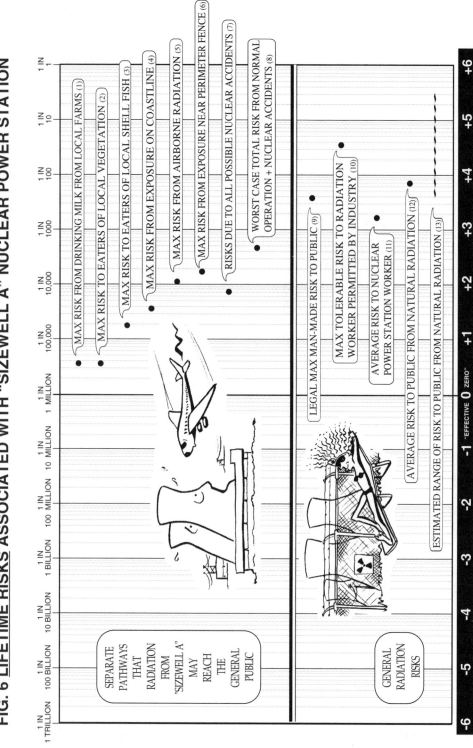

SEPARATE PATHWAYS THAT RADIATION FROM "SIZEWELL A" MAY REACH THE GENERAL PUBLIC

MAX RISK FROM DRINKING MILK FROM LOCAL FARMS (1)
MAX RISK TO EATERS OF LOCAL VEGETATION (2)
MAX RISK TO EATERS OF LOCAL SHELL FISH (3)
MAX RISK FROM EXPOSURE ON COASTLINE (4)
MAX RISK FROM AIRBORNE RADIATION (5)
MAX RISK FROM EXPOSURE NEAR PERIMETER FENCE (6)
RISKS DUE TO ALL POSSIBLE NUCLEAR ACCIDENTS (7)
WORST CASE TOTAL RISK FROM NORMAL OPERATION + NUCLEAR ACCIDENTS (8)

GENERAL RADIATION RISKS

LEGAL MAX MAN-MADE RISK TO PUBLIC (9)
MAX TOLERABLE RISK TO RADIATION WORKER PERMITTED BY INDUSTRY (10)
AVERAGE RISK TO NUCLEAR POWER STATION WORKER (11)
AVERAGE RISK TO PUBLIC FROM NATURAL RADIATION (12)
ESTIMATED RANGE OF RISK TO PUBLIC FROM NATURAL RADIATION (13)

1 IN 1 | 1 IN 10 | 1 IN 100 | 1 IN 1000 | 1 IN 10,000 | 1 IN 100,000 | 1 IN 1 MILLION | 1 IN 10 MILLION | 1 IN 100 MILLION | 1 IN 1 BILLION | 1 IN 10 BILLION | 1 IN 100 BILLION | 1 IN 1 TRILLION

+6 | +5 | +4 | +3 | +2 | +1 | 0 "EFFECTIVE ZERO" | -1 | -2 | -3 | -4 | -5 | -6

(THESE RISKS ARE CALCULATED ASSUMING A CONTINUOUS EXPOSURE THROUGH A LIFETIME)

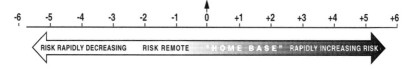

But, having said that, it must be remembered that because of the way the law requires record keeping, the figures we get are for *the maximum possible calculated figures for each category of risk.* Unless you are one of Sizewell's neighbors, **AND** you drink more milk from local farms than anyone else for the whole of your lifetime, **AND** you eat the most vegetables grown in the immediate neighborhood, **AND** stuff yourself on local shellfish (more than anyone else), **AND** you spend your time walking the perimeter fence (also more than anyone else), then the figures do not apply to you or any other real person.

## What the Anti-nuclear Lobby Says

To be fair, we invited the British branch of Greenpeace and other environmental groups to use the scale to express their own appraisal of the risks to the public from nuclear power generation. We have also offered to publish this as a way of enabling the public to visually compare the different conclusions that a pro- and anti-nuclear group provide on the same issue.

However, despite our good relations with both parties, this has not been possible. Greenpeace in

discussions and by letter, has pointed out that, when it comes to risks from a nuclear power station it is *not* a matter of how those risks may compare with other activities or industrial practices, but "it is solely a matter of whether that risk can in itself be justified - i.e. that the benefits from the practice outweigh the detriment." ... "Ultimately, Greenpeace's position is that the risks posed by the nuclear power industry, both in terms of routine and accidental releases of radioactivity, are unjustifiable and unacceptable."

Since the main purpose of this book is to introduce the scale to all parties, we have tried not to take sides on any issue. So while we make no editorial response to these comments, we repeat that we would still welcome anti-nuclear activists' interpretation of the figures or their own estimates as to what level of relative "detriment" a nuclear generator poses.

Our investigations have revealed one constant factor that fuels the continuing disagreements between the two parties. That is the high level of distrust and suspicion that the anti-nuclear movement feels for the nuclear industry. Clearly our friends at Greenpeace have every right to consider the industry's figures (or our

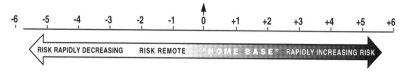

THE PALING PERSPECTIVE SCALE

interpretations) to be flawed, and we can only repeat our genuine effort to record all reasonable estimates of risk levels along with the evidence for such alternative positions.

It occurs to us that perhaps both parties would better resolve their differences if the nuclear industry, using a mutually respected facilitator, was totally open in sharing its available figures with Greenpeace.

If nothing else, it seems reasonable that the anti-nuclear lobby has a right to know what odds there are for possible accidents in the industry. Greenpeace feels that crucial information on the safety incidents for British nuclear plants are withheld from them on the grounds that it is "commercially confidential." Regardless of who is right, sooner or later society is going to expect some estimate of detriment from the anti-nuclear groups and a total openness of safety records from the industry. When all this information is available, it can be reflected on the scale.

Many who oppose nuclear power are less concerned about whether a nuclear generator will melt down than they are about whether the long-lasting nuclear wastes that are produced can be safely stored. However, the scale could also be

FIG. 7  RISK OF BECOMING A CRIME STATISTIC IN ONE YEAR

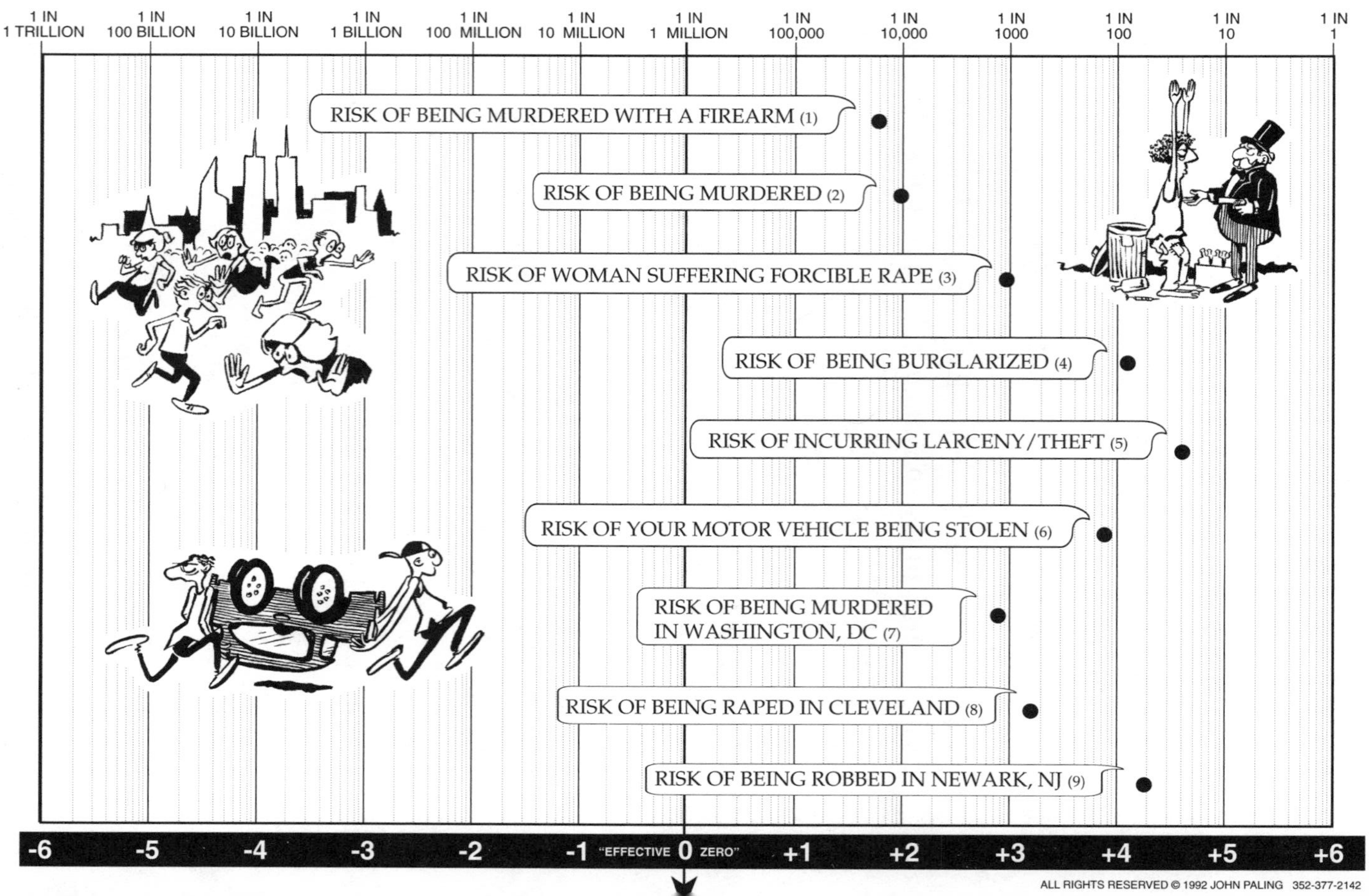

RISK OF BEING MURDERED WITH A FIREARM (1)

RISK OF BEING MURDERED (2)

RISK OF WOMAN SUFFERING FORCIBLE RAPE (3)

RISK OF BEING BURGLARIZED (4)

RISK OF INCURRING LARCENY/THEFT (5)

RISK OF YOUR MOTOR VEHICLE BEING STOLEN (6)

RISK OF BEING MURDERED IN WASHINGTON, DC (7)

RISK OF BEING RAPED IN CLEVELAND (8)

RISK OF BEING ROBBED IN NEWARK, NJ (9)

1 IN 1 | 1 IN 10 | 1 IN 100 | 1 IN 1000 | 1 IN 10,000 | 1 IN 100,000 | 1 IN 1 MILLION | 1 IN 10 MILLION | 1 IN 100 MILLION | 1 IN 1 BILLION | 1 IN 10 BILLION | 1 IN 100 BILLION | 1 IN 1 TRILLION

+6  +5  +4  +3  +2  +1  0 "EFFECTIVE ZERO"  -1  -2  -3  -4  -5  -6

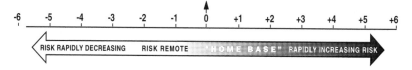

THE PALING PERSPECTIVE SCALE

used to record the levels of risk involved with the different methods of nuclear waste disposal. Such a tool would provide the public with valuable insight on how relatively risky the whole area of nuclear technology is.

Lastly, a nuclear skeptic can rightly point out that a small level of risk of a very serious accident happening (say a "-3" risk of a power station melt down that would devastate a whole community) is more important than a higher chance (say a "+3") of a less serious event happening (like food poisoning) that might affect far fewer people. This too is a fair point, but such calculations are already taken into consideration by those whose job is to manage risks for society (see also Risk Factors, page 107.)

*So there it is.* A simple account intended to demonstrate how the levels of risk associated with one of our most complex and controversial industries can be understood intuitively by the public with the help of a perspective scale.

We readily admit that any such scale does have its limitations but we are confident that it offers the public a big step forward, away from the mass confusion that typically exists. And, what's more, it is not restricted to environmental risks.

*"Some of
society's risks are
of a far higher order
of significance than many
environmental hazards."*

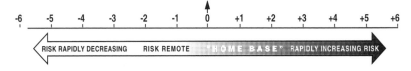

# - 9 -

# PUTTING SOCIETAL RISKS INTO PERSPECTIVE

We started out on a personal journey of discovery seeking a greater understanding of the relative importance of various environmental risks.

Initially the goal was simply to find an honest way to demonstrate to the public that we were in danger of scaring ourselves needlessly about minuscule risks far below those we ignore in our daily lives! However, in working on this project, we have come up with a scale that serves as a window to focus and frame, not just environmental risks, but all types of threats and hazards. What has resulted is a perspective scale that conveniently lets us put pollution risks into perspective on the same scale that can show many other risks that impact society. (For example, see Fig. 7, page 70).

**This scale also offers a way to put many other aspects of our lives in perspective.**

# FIG. 8 THE GAP BETWEEN MEDIA HEADLINERS AND MR. AVERAGE

"THE AVERAGE JOE ZONE"

This is the area of probability for most of the events that most people will ever experience.

"THE BOBBIT ZONE" MEDIA MANIA

This reflects the range of probability for all those "one of a kind" events that often dominate the media.

POINTS HERE SHOW WHAT HAPPENS TO 50% OF THE POPULATION (3)

ODDS OF ANYTHING HAPPENING TO ONLY ONE PERSON IN WHOLE U.S.A. POPULATION (2)

ODDS OF ANYTHING HAPPENING TO ONLY ONE PERSON IN WHOLE WORLD POPULATION (1)

1 IN 1 | 1 IN 10 | 1 IN 100 | 1 IN 1000 | 1 IN 10,000 | 1 IN 100,000 | 1 IN 1 MILLION | 1 IN 10 MILLION | 1 IN 100 MILLION | 1 IN 1 BILLION | 1 IN 10 BILLION | 1 IN 100 BILLION | 1 IN 1 TRILLION

+6 | +5 | +4 | +3 | +2 | +1 | 0 "EFFECTIVE ZERO" | -1 | -2 | -3 | -4 | -5 | -6

Page 74

Perhaps one of the most revealing insights is to remind ourselves that the media (responding to what we all find fascinating) often fills its columns with stories that are newsworthy in part because they are *so* exceptional. The odds of many of these events happening in the average person's life are truly minute. Yet because we hear so much about some of these stories, it is sometimes easy to be mislead about the likelihood of some similar tragedy happening to us.

When you chart on the scale the incidents that have occurred to one person in the U.S. or one person in the world, they show up in the "-2" to a "-4" area. Friends call this "The Bobbitt Zone" after a bizarre incident that dominated the American media's attention for many weeks, but to the best of our knowledge, has only ever occurred to one person. (See Fig. 8, page 74).

In contrast, when you show the odds of something happening to the average person on the scale (or what is happening to 50 percent of the people), then the odds of 1 in 2 show up very close to a "+6." The gulf is enormous!

# FIG. 9 RISKS FROM A U.S. LIFESTYLE

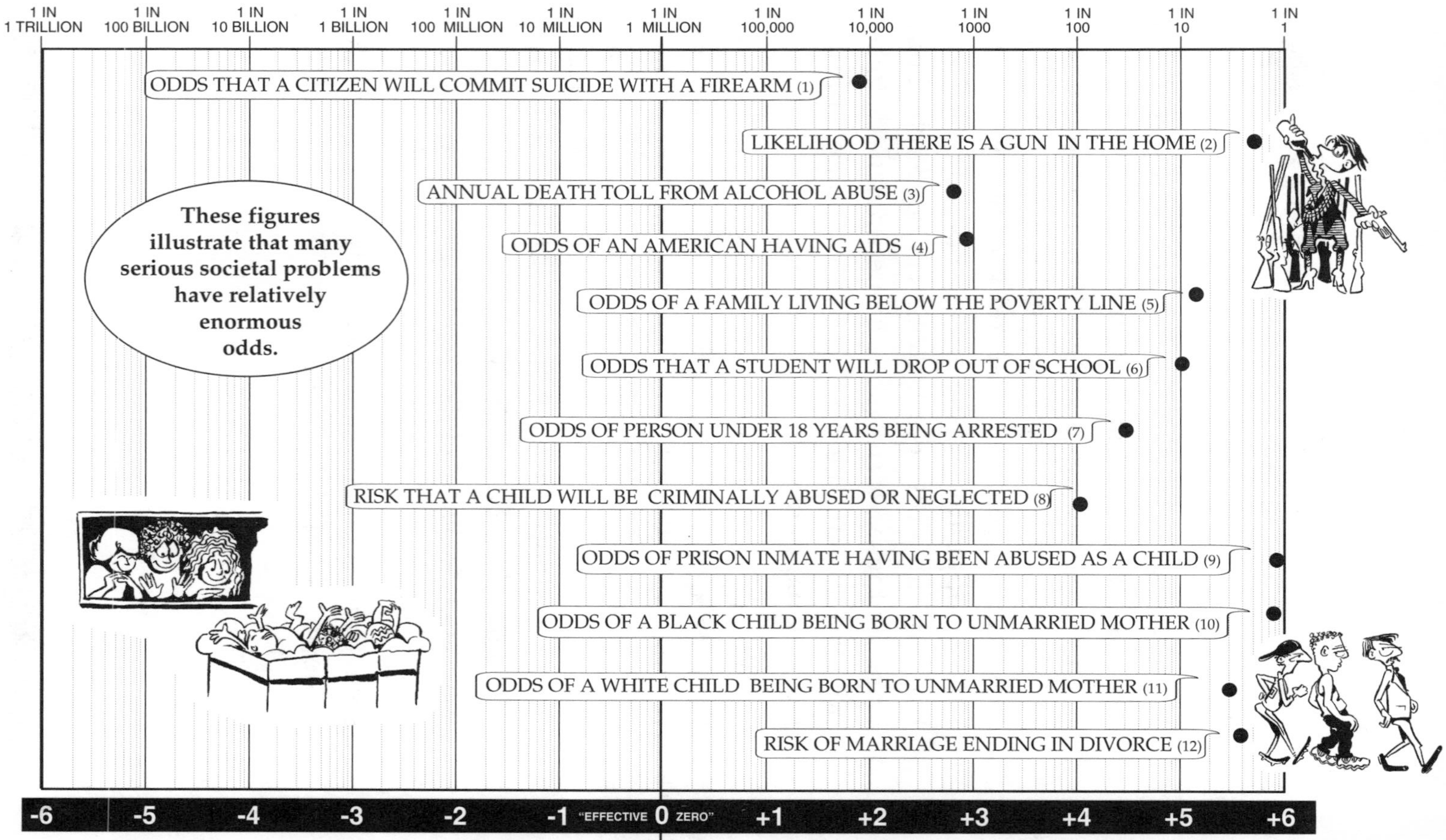

ODDS THAT A CITIZEN WILL COMMIT SUICIDE WITH A FIREARM (1)

LIKELIHOOD THERE IS A GUN IN THE HOME (2)

ANNUAL DEATH TOLL FROM ALCOHOL ABUSE (3)

ODDS OF AN AMERICAN HAVING AIDS (4)

ODDS OF A FAMILY LIVING BELOW THE POVERTY LINE (5)

ODDS THAT A STUDENT WILL DROP OUT OF SCHOOL (6)

ODDS OF PERSON UNDER 18 YEARS BEING ARRESTED (7)

RISK THAT A CHILD WILL BE CRIMINALLY ABUSED OR NEGLECTED (8)

ODDS OF PRISON INMATE HAVING BEEN ABUSED AS A CHILD (9)

ODDS OF A BLACK CHILD BEING BORN TO UNMARRIED MOTHER (10)

ODDS OF A WHITE CHILD BEING BORN TO UNMARRIED MOTHER (11)

RISK OF MARRIAGE ENDING IN DIVORCE (12)

These figures illustrate that many serious societal problems have relatively enormous odds.

1 IN 1 TRILLION | 1 IN 100 BILLION | 1 IN 10 BILLION | 1 IN 1 BILLION | 1 IN 100 MILLION | 1 IN 10 MILLION | 1 IN 1 MILLION | 1 IN 100,000 | 1 IN 10,000 | 1 IN 1000 | 1 IN 100 | 1 IN 10 | 1 IN 1

-6  -5  -4  -3  -2  -1  0 "EFFECTIVE ZERO"  +1  +2  +3  +4  +5  +6

With that in mind, it is most revealing to put on the scale some of the social phenomena that have been surveyed in the U.S. (See Fig. 9 page. 76) These are societal issues that may not be risks in the public's immediate meaning of the word, but to our mind, represent enormous threats to the stability and social fabric of our society in view of their ultimate consequences.

**The Paling Perspective Scale[SM] is a tool that can help us decide what is really worth worrying about in our modern world. It is an antidote for a generation that seems to have an overwhelming number of concerns that cry out for our attention, yet less and less time to focus on the really serious hazards of our lifestyles.**

It is interesting because the most acute short-term risks turn out not to be the traditional environmental worries like nuclear power and "Super Fund" sites but instead involve problems with society. If these challenges are to be solved, they usually require accepting personal responsibility for controlling our own behaviors. It is so much easier to blame "them" and to look for

"the enemy" over the hill!

What really is killing people in the U.S.A., according to the Harvard Center for Risk Analysis, is **smoking** (annual death toll in U.S. = 300,000), **alcohol abuse** (annual death toll = 150,000), **highway travel** (annual death toll = 45,000) and **homicides** (20,000 deaths annually). Indoor air toxins probably kill 6,000; outdoor toxins probably take out another 3,000; while pesticide residues on food are estimated to cause about 3,000 fatalities. To this, I would add that as of August 1996 the U.S.A. has 554,000 reported cases of **AIDS** (annual death toll = 40,000)

## Environmentalists and Businesses: Working Together for a Better Society

It is possible that the next big challenge for environmentalists is to remove our green blinders and see environmental problems as part of a wider context of societal needs. Although our scale started out as an environmental communications tool, it may be that one of its long-term benefits will be to show environmental risks (and needs) alongside the other risks and needs of our communities.

This broader perspective could have significant benefits to businesses, too. One of the criticisms

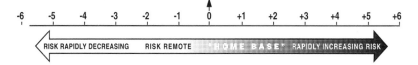

that environmentalists have thrown at the business community is that every one of them declares that their own activities pose no serious risks, yet no one seems willing to point to areas where real risks from industries to the community really do exist.

The recognition that some of society's risks are of a far higher order of significance than many environmental hazards gives businesses an opportunity to do two things that would both help them as well as making further contributions to society.

First, businesses can use the scale to clearly point out to their communities how the risks associated with their operations relate to other daily risks of living. We believe that all businesses, instead of appearing to puff in denial, should admit that their activities *do* involve risks and cause some measure of pollution (as the scale show exists for virtually every other aspect of living). Risks caused by industry should <u>not</u> be ignored or sidestepped, but should be put in perspective.

Responsible businesses should be (and be seen as) both concerned and accountable for their impact on society. At the same time, in transforming the issue to one of "how relatively risky is it?" they can point out that they see societal needs being more urgent in view of their position on the scale. They

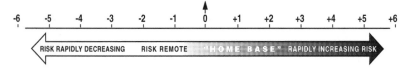

THE PALING PERSPECTIVE SCALE

| -6 | -5 | -4 | -3 | -2 | -1 | 0 | +1 | +2 | +3 | +4 | +5 | +6 |

RISK RAPIDLY DECREASING    RISK REMOTE    "HOME BASE"    RAPIDLY INCREASING RISK

might choose to focus some of their local charitable contributions to those issues that their local community feels pose the greatest relative risks. By doing this, the local organizations not only get help from the corporate community but also gain an education in comparative risk assessment. Hopefully, this should reflect well on the relatively minor risks that businesses impose, while at the same time enabling everyone - environmentalists, businesses and community members - to begin to work together to provide real benefits by addressing the biggest problems first.

We acknowledge that some of the biggest environmental risks to our planet cannot be fitted on our scale at this time (see page 89). We strongly share the grave concerns about conserving endangered species, combatting climate change and addressing overpopulation issues but our focus is on pollution concerns here.

In our opinion, environmentalists may not be consistent with reality if we appear to exaggerate the importance of some pollution issues while we remain silent about the much greater hazards that exist in our communities.

Realistically, citizens under extreme duress can hardly be expected to take care of the environment

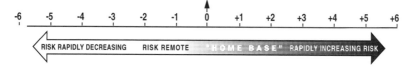

when they can barely take care of themselves and are confronting greater societal problems on a daily basis in their own communities.

Perhaps the scale may help put the whole topic of risk in perspective and remind us that problems associated with education, crime, child abuse, drugs, family responsibility and urban renewal are equally deserving of our nation's attention and resources. It has certainly been an eye-opener for the authors to view our world through the prism of the perspective scale and be confronted with the enormity of our societal problems.

Already we have come a long way together as we have explained this totally new approach to putting the risks of life into perspective. Right now, the reader is probably thinking, "This scale looks incredibly helpful at first sight but I've still got some concerns and problems about the validity of using something so seductively simple for the public." So next let us address some of the questions that people have asked prior to embracing The Paling Perspective Scale℠ and using it for themselves.

*"Risks*
*caused by industry*
*should <u>not</u> be ignored*
*or sidestepped,*
*but they should be put*
*into perspective."*

THE PALING PERSPECTIVE SCALE

# - 10 -

# ANY QUESTIONS?

*"Whose figures are you going to trust? Different groups will always choose the method of risk assessment that suits their own interests; businesses will pitch a figure for low risk, activists will claim high risks."*

This is an important point and undeniably probable. Our suggestion is that initially you put figures from all sides on the chart. Most people are surprised to find that our scale (like the Richter Scale for earthquakes) results in differences becoming compressed together with the result that the approximate *zone* of the risk in question will probably still be evident. Thus, despite the differences, the exercise will still provide helpful comparative information.

Soon we anticipate that, for current controversial issues, first the technical and later the popular media will seek out the basis of each side's calculations and will define a middle ground position. A similar "checking of the facts" is done to some degree to provide balance to political claims made in election times.

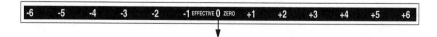

**"Businesses and agencies measure risks in terms of how they relate to government regulations and not in terms of the relative odds that would fit on your chart. How did you come up with your figures?"**

Admittedly, it is sometimes hard to get information about the odds for some industrial risks. However, government officials have said so much about the desirability of involving citizens in understanding risks that agencies can reasonably be asked to explain to what level of risk a particular law is supposed to protect. Then you can work out what the odds are for, say, some pollutant that is half the level permitted by law.

We consciously avoided setting ourselves up to execute new assessments of risks in this first book. Instead, we have taken figures from the published literature and, if necessary, recalculated them to be comparable to others. It is obviously important to ensure that, as far as possible, we are really comparing like with like. One publication may have expressed a particular risk in terms of annual incidents, while another might have been expressed in terms of lifetime risks. In such a case, it is fairly easy to do a calculation to express both in a common unit for comparative purposes.

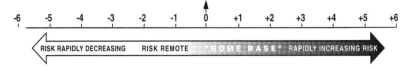

*"Aren't you concerned that professionals are going to disapprove of seeing a risk expressed by just one single point on the scale? They much prefer to state a risk as falling within some range and they're not going to like this!"*

Practitioners know well that all estimates of risk are just that - estimates. And estimates carried out with different assumptions and by different reputable scientists can produce quite a wide level of uncertainty. However, it is simple to reflect the level of variability on our scale as a line extending between the range of possible alternatives. For detailed communications, that is obviously the best and most desirable way to use the scale.

However, *in order to simplify the public's immediate comprehension of the basic principles of this scale*, here we typically quote a single point rather than trying to show the range between the upper and lower bounds for each estimate.

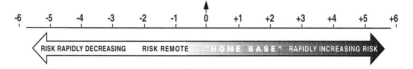

## *"Why don't you __always__ show risks for a lifetime since citizens are concerned for long-term effects - not just one year of exposure?"*

Citizens may be exposed to industrial hazards for long periods and activists correctly suggest that we should look at a lifetime of exposure if our scale is to help society face realities. Lifetime risks can usually be simply approximated by multiplying the risk level for one year by the number of years that a person might be exposed.

However, this multiplier factor needs to be different for different hazards. For example, sometimes a 70-year lifetime of exposure to a hazard (like drinking tap water in a particular neighborhood) is appropriate, while for other hazards (like driving a car) 50 years might be a more reasonable "lifetime." Again, for other hazards (like mountain climbing or playing professional football) a 10-year lifetime of exposure might be more appropriate.

This variability makes it easier to compare *annual* risks. We intend and recommend the scale be used to compare annual risks in most circumstances. When used for lifetime risks any reference to the "Home Base" area should be increased accordingly.

*"How do you answer experts from the business world who feel that one in 100,000 and not one in a million - would be a fairer 'Effective Zero' point?"*

We acknowledge that there is a valid case for this opinion, given the levels of caution already built into methods of calculating risks. However, since our prime goal is to produce a scale that is accepted by the general public, we are anxious to go at least "one step further" on the side of ultra-safety than might otherwise be considered necessary.

Since our scale features such an overprotective zero point for annual risks, it will thus immediately permit businesses with emissions that are effectively innocuous to provide evidence that they lie below our "Effective Zero." This will reinforce the minuscule perspective of such risks and invite a more appropriate response to the cost/benefit equation involved in their production.

Coincidentally, The U.S. Environmental Protection Agency, working from different criteria, sets its safety standards for regulations so that risks between one in one million and one in 1,000 are variously considered as acceptable for all practical purposes. On our scale, that is between

"0" and "+3." Hence the public should be strongly reassured that anything less than "0" on our scale is truly "safe" for all practical purposes.

What society views as "safe" depends in part on what the public and regulators feel is a comfortable *balance* between any particular risk and the benefits that we gain by undertaking it. That is the main criterion involved in deciding to accept the risk of flying or to accept chlorinating our water supply.

### *"What type of risks is the scale best for?"*

Undoubtedly our Perspective Scale is most useful when considerations of pollution and health risks are at stake. It also provides a fresh, powerful perspective for other societal problems that, because of their constant exposure in different guises, have frequently lost their impact.

Since these are the areas that businesses, regulators and environmentalists are most often in contention, our scale should have an immediate value in defining the reasonable level of concern that might be appropriate.

## "Will this Perspective Scale work for all environmental risks?"

Currently the scale is unlikely to add new perspectives for the public on such key areas as overpopulation, global climate change or loss of species diversity.

To try and calculate the risks in these areas involves so many subjective judgments and complexities that an enormous level of genuine disagreement is likely. In these cases where there are such wide levels of uncertainty, it is not very helpful to try to plot these risks on the scale.

It should be noted, however, that the problem lies not in the value of the scale but in the limits of the experts' ability to assess and quantify the consequences of changes in these crucial areas for humans. When it is possible to assess more accurately the real risks involved, it will become doubly important to present them on a perspective scale to appreciate how wisely we are apportioning society's financial resources in relation to other concerns.

In the author's personal view, these global environmental issues do indeed present enormous concerns for the future. Even though they cannot currently be measured now, we envision that they will show up in some form on the scale within the next decade.

### *"Doesn't it bother you that this scale ignores the risks to the non-human inhabitants on our planet?"*

Yes. All my years of experience as a biologist have left me with a deeply held conviction that society cannot continue indefinitely pursuing our non-sustainable lifestyles. Part of this trend leads inevitably to further loss of habitat and the inevitable extinction of more species. Currently, however, I cannot offer figures on the chart to quantify this risk.

Pragmatically, I recognize that the key environmental choices affecting the future of our planet will most likely be made on the basis of human self interest. Thus, I do not envision this scale being used to address the risks to non human species on our planet at this time.

However, in the future, I believe this will change as scientists will be able to give a convincing accounting for risks to humans as we cause further environmental stresses, increasing ecological degradation and further loss of species.

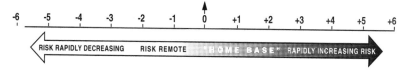

## *"Why doesn't this Perspective Scale distinguish between voluntary versus involuntary risks?"*

It is well established from traditional teachings of risk communication that, in general, people's level of response to a potential risk is NOT mainly influenced by the odds of the event actually happening. Studies by Sandman and others (see page 125) have shown that the intensity of the public's concern is more determined by issues such as whether the hazard is undertaken *voluntarily*, say playing football, compared with a similar level of risk that an individual is *involuntarily* exposed to, such as fumes from a neighboring business.

However, while accepting that communicators need an understanding of the factors influencing the public's perception of risk, it is our position that *there is nothing more important than communicating the best estimates of the ACTUAL levels of the risks involved.* And this is what our scale was designed for.

This scale will always be most valuable when it is used for comparing involuntary risks with other involuntary risks - and so on. However, the Home Base Zone in Fig. 2 shows both voluntary and involuntary risks and so we feel that that zone is fairly characterized for comparative purposes.

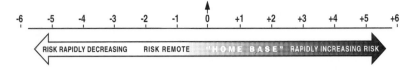

*"Your scale is 'comparing apples with oranges.' How can you justify putting so many different types of risks embodying different levels of certainty on the same scale?"*

We are aware that there remain several important concerns that this simplified outline does not address. Issues such as comparing estimates of dissimilar risks with different degrees of predictability; quantifying the hazards of low, persistent levels of exposure; calculating the likely effects of exposure to humans based only on laboratory studies on rats; acknowledging our ignorance about the possibility of aggregated risks: all these complicate attempts at relative risk communication for the public.

However, most of these criticisms reflect a problem for risk assessments in general and are difficulties that our simple scale cannot be expected to solve immediately. As we have said before, our approach will always be most valuable when it uses the best research available, when it compares like with like, and views new risks alongside a Home Base Zone that the user is comfortable about accepting as part of their own daily life.

*"Did you anticipate that neither the environmental activists nor some industries would welcome this because it doesn't suit their vested interests?"*

In the real world, this is one political problem that we had not anticipated fully. We are finding that some parties with vested interests are not sure that they *want* to change the status quo. Some business groups are concerned that when a clearer priority of risks *is* established, some of their members will become even more sharply focused as the target of the media's criticisms. This scale may clear away some of the fog of uncertainty that may have helped diffuse some of the previous criticisms.

Some environmental groups, on the other hand, have found benefit in publicizing all manner of risks as being of the highest significance. As well as reflecting sincere fears, this also serves to keep their funding primed. Skeptics have argued that it may not be beneficial to have comparative figures showing, say, the low levels of real risk for alar on apples or nuclear power generation when many of their members may be impassioned about these issues.

*"Aren't you worried that this approach to risk communication may show a reassuring position for a risk today but later that same thing turns out to have been very serious? History is full of examples of that."*

This is a real possibility. Frankly, it is one of the enduring fears of professionals as well as ordinary citizens. It can be supported from past experiences such as X-rays in the 50s to alpha rays in the 90s. Skeptics have the right to caution that we just don't know enough yet to recognize all the "nasties" that a new technology can produce for society.

While this concern is understandable, any scale is inevitably limited by the extent of current knowledge. Sadly, we cannot predict the future. We can only record what we know now and keep an eye open for new, as yet unidentified, hazards from our contemporary life styles.

But society's understanding and knowledge of risk issues is rapidly growing. Both the public and businesses will certainly become more sophisticated about balancing the relative risks in our lives. There is now widespread acceptance, at least in theory, that future public policy decisions should try to take into account the application of cost/benefit analyses so that our resources are targeted to give the greatest protection.

THE PALING PERSPECTIVE SCALE

Although there are several practical difficulties to putting this concept into place as rapidly as many businesses would like, the logic of basing regulations on some assessment of the costs and the benefits is now firmly in place. And the upshot of all this is that citizens throughout the world will have an opportunity to learn more and more about relative risks.

Since this technique for putting risks into perspective is so different from what the public has been offered before, we see ourselves as part of this new movement of education, empowerment and democracy.

We sincerely hope The Paling Perspective Scale[SM] will help citizens make better decisions about the risks in their lives and will help businesses by serving as a valuable tool both to communicate and to assess risks.

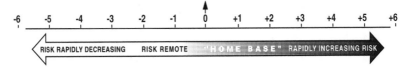

THE PALING PERSPECTIVE SCALE

-6  -5  -4  -3  -2  -1  0  +1  +2  +3  +4  +5  +6

RISK RAPIDLY DECREASING     RISK REMOTE     "HOME BASE"  RAPIDLY INCREASING RISK

*" Our main message
is that all risks
should be seen in
perspective"*

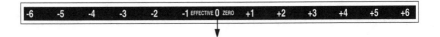

-6  -5  -4  -3  -2  -1 EFFECTIVE 0 ZERO  +1  +2  +3  +4  +5  +6

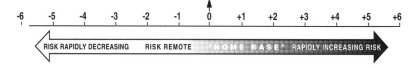

# - 11 -

# HOW TO VIEW THE NEXT RISK YOU HEAR ABOUT

Once you become aware of the hordes of hazards in everyday life, you begin to see and hear risks in a new light!

• First, you notice that the majority of dilemmas reported by the news media are relayed to the public as dangers with no mention of *levels* of risk. Rarely does a report on risk give a measure of the **actual** estimate of something happening in the **actual** circumstances for the local population (a true risk assessment).

• If the reported hazard does not give any estimate of levels of risk, then a fair response is to say:

*"Okay, this may be a really important concern but the fact that there may be minute quantities of a poison present doesn't mean a thing in itself. The 'actual dose' the public may be exposed to is the only thing that will decide whether it is a poison or a panic."*

Before you can assess how *relatively* risky it is, you

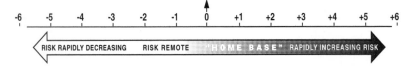

THE PALING PERSPECTIVE SCALE

need more information. Frankly, without some estimate of risk, your source could be crying "wolf" (or "Alar" or "nerve gas")!

• Keep things in perspective. Recognize that no individual can take time to follow up on every possible risk and that our government has well staffed agencies who are charged with the responsibility to protect the public and workers' health and safety.

• But, if your intuition tells you that you are dealing with a risk that you want to follow up on, then the first step would be to ask for information - including some estimate on the level of risk- from the experts that are supposed to protect the public.

• Also, this is a reasonable request to ask of whomever suggested that it was serious in the first place, perhaps a media reporter. Equally, it is a question that can validly be posed to any business, regulator or environmental group that claims to have information relevant to the issue in question.

• A helpful way to phrase your questions might be: "What are all the possible risks that you know of that might affect my community because of (the issue in question)?" Then "What is your estimate of

# THE PALING PERSPECTIVE SCALE

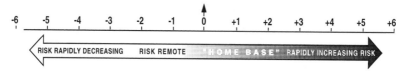

the odds in a million, on an annual basis of (whatever is your concern) increasing these risks to me and my family (or community)?"

• As you research to find estimates of the level of "your" risk, you need to be alert to the precise circumstances and conditions that were defined in calculating the figures: risk for one year?, for one age group?, for one country?, etc. to try to best match your circumstances.

• In particular, remember that for consistency of comparison when using the chart, you should try to compare like with like. If you find figures quoted on the basis of a lifetime's risk, then reduce the figure by the number of years in a typical "lifetime" of exposure. (For example, 70 years for drinking water, 30 years for taking birth control pills etc.)

• Once you have obtained a figure for the estimated level of risk that the hazard represents, then you can put it on our scale in its *approximate* position and get a general feel for how serious it is compared to all your other risks in life.

• If the *annual* risk level is around or below a "+0" on the scale, then, unless your circumstances render you to be exceptionally vulnerable, don't worry, be happy. You should instead be concerned with other

## THE PALING PERSPECTIVE SCALE

risks that are more likely to have a serious effect on your life. Also, be aware that there are many risks in society that fall in the "+1" and "+2" ranges, and by and large, people in the Western society live good, long and healthy lives. Annual risks of over "+2" on the scale signify "be cautious and take care."
Above "+3", take appropriate avoiding actions - unless there are commensurate big benefits such as most medical procedures.

### What it all comes down to is this:

Life is full of risks which, no matter what we do, cannot be brought down to zero. But our message is NOT to suggest therefore that the public should not worry about risks or that they should stop making demands on businesses. On the contrary, our mission is to reinforce the acceptance that risks are part of being alive and our goal is to focus on how society deals with this reality.

The fact that there are risks to everyone's life is not just a theoretical fact that somehow can be swept under the rug by putting figures on a chart. We need to recognize that every day, individuals and families are being torn apart by terrible, grievous events that, yes may be remote when it comes to the odds, but they really do happen to real

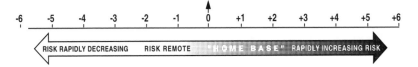

THE PALING PERSPECTIVE SCALE

people. It might be you or me tomorrow and the people that are affected need help and sympathy and love to get them through. This may take the form of traditional values like family support, financial reserves or appropriate insurances.

Our main purpose is to reinforce the belief that all risks should be seen in perspective and to encourage an open discussion about the implications of seeing threats in terms of *relative* risks.

The odds of some terrible event happening to us are determined not just by how dangerous some situation might be but how much we expose ourselves to risks by virtue of our behavior. In other words, once citizens get interested in researching real risks, they can often make an enormous difference to their own safety by taking the responsibility to reduce their exposure (move further away from hurricanes, wear a seat belt, use a condom etc.)

In these confusing times, The Paling Perspective Scale[SM] is offered as a simple way for the public and businesses to make better decisions based on the realities of life.

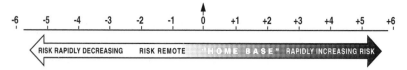

## THE PALING PERSPECTIVE SCALE

-6  -5  -4  -3  -2  -1  0  +1  +2  +3  +4  +5  +6

RISK RAPIDLY DECREASING    RISK REMOTE    "HOME BASE"  RAPIDLY INCREASING RISK

*"Don't tell the public that everything is "safe". Instead start by explaining that everything has some risk attached to it"*

-6  -5  -4  -3  -2  -1 EFFECTIVE 0 ZERO  +1  +2  +3  +4  +5  +6

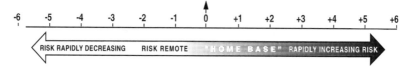

# -12-

# HOW RISK COMMUNICATORS CAN BENEFIT FROM A PERSPECTIVE SCALE

Most businesses are so anxious to justify the safety of their operations that they can get into serious trouble by claiming that there is absolutely zero risk for the public. Not only can this rapidly lead down the embarrassing path to being proved wrong, but it can easily result in more alarm being generated than ever need have existed in the first place!

You only have to go back to the summer of 1996 for a vivid example of what can go wrong. The British government was suddenly faced with a national panic about a possible outbreak of so-called "Mad Cow Disease". It hastily announced that the meat supply was completely safe, only to back down later and qualify its position. This lead to an already concerned public perceiving that they had not been told the truth in the first place and to suspect that the problem was far more troubling than the authorities were letting on. Fanned by media coverage, the public's fears took off like a fire in a gas station and soon the Europeans joined in by banning most British beef products, all at enormous cost to the industry. The panic was only quelled by the announcement that millions of cattle were to be slaughtered and disposed of - as a safety precaution!

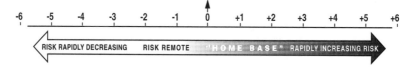

THE PALING PERSPECTIVE SCALE

Our advice is for corporate communicators to take the reverse approach. Don't tell the public that everything is "safe". Instead start by explaining that everything has some risk attached to it. Accept the reality of our first law - *there is no such thing as a risk free life style*- and concede that your operations in some way or other might theoretically represent a very small risk to the community.

For anyone in business who is doubtful about the truth of this mind set, it might be helpful to remember that there is a lot we don't know about risks yet. For example, here are just three areas that I think should give cause for appropriate caution. First it is impossible to deny that new chemicals *may* be reacting in the environment to produce new poisons that we know nothing about as yet. Second, if your community includes people who are hyper-allergic, they *might* defy statistics calculated for the average Joe. And thirdly, recent research suggests that fetuses have totally different chemical sensitivities from adults - yet our "safety tests" are typically done on adult animals, so we *may* be causing harm that does not show up until years later.

So it is more truthful as well as more productive to admit that, in truth, most things in life come with some minute risk attached to them and that you are very willing to discuss all community concerns in this light. This understanding moves the discussion forward from "Is this really a risk?" to "How relatively risky is this compared to all the other risks in our lives – and what shall we do about it?"

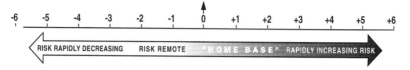

Because The Paling Perspective Scale[SM] is so easily understood, it is possible to put it into the hands of your stakeholders so they can put their own figures on the chart along with other risks that they feel they are at home with. This empowers those individuals who really do want to understand and has the added benefit that both sides are at last speaking the same "language". Businesses can also gain trust and respect in the community by suggesting that citizens get their own estimates of the risks that they are concerned about and put them on the scale along with the company's figures.

If this open approach sounds like giving in, then please appreciate that at the very least, it moves the discussion away from purely emotional anecdotes and into the area of looking at the real relative risks. This has rarely been achieved with other methods of corporate risk communication.

More likely your company's openness, coupled with the empowerment of citizens to sort things out for themselves, will lead to a new dimension in helping your community in putting the real risks of the real world into perspective.

This is only one aspect of our new approach to risk communication for businesses which turns the more typical approach of denying risk on its head. For more information, please see page 153.

THE PALING PERSPECTIVE SCALE

-6   -5   -4   -3   -2   -1   0   +1   +2   +3   +4   +5   +6

RISK RAPIDLY DECREASING    RISK REMOTE    HOME BASE℠   RAPIDLY INCREASING RISK

*..... But for businesses' internal use, The Basic Paling Perspective Scale℠ is not enough...*

-6   -5   -4   -3   -2   -1 EFFECTIVE 0 ZERO   +1   +2   +3   +4   +5   +6

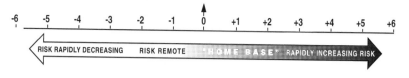

# -13-

# RISK FACTORS FOR BUSINESSES ON THE PALING PERSPECTIVE SCALE℠

Although this chapter is mainly intended for executives in business, everyone is welcome to join us in our journey as we take our scale one giant step further forward. While the basic version of the scale has great value for communicating with the general public, it does not fully solve major corporations' need for a quick way of assessing the relative importance of many of the risks they encounter.

Given the increasing uncertainties for all of today's companies, proactive executives seek ways to answer crucial questions like: *"How can I create greater value for my company by trying to identify those risks that may derail our business and then prioritize which of them merit most of our resources?"*

To meet this challenge, we offer a more sophisticated version of the scale. To understand why this is necessary and how it operates, I must first review what the basic scale is good for and then explain why, as it stands, it does not answer all the needs of businesses.

The first part of this book focuses on describing a simple communications tool to help non-technical people

put risks into perspective by using the basic version of The Paling Perspective Scale<sup>SM</sup>. We have found that this simple version is ideal for corporate communicators to use for explaining to concerned communities how a particular hazard actually compares to the many other risks that citizens acknowledge they are "at home" with.

The basic scale is so valuable and powerful because, by putting their own figures from all sorts of sources on the chart, the public can take ownership of it and can accept what it shows. This citizen empowerment is of enormous importance to the success of executives dealing with communities on contentious issues.

Empowering the public in this way gets around one of the biggest obstacles that industry has always faced when it has attempted to discuss risks with members of the community. When the public looks at risks for themselves through the window of a perspective scale, the discussions move away from anecdotes and towards accepting a real world full of thousands of real but minute risks that have to be put into perspective.

In the past, most businesses would confront an inflamed local community by trying to share their knowledge and experience at a level that the public could understand. But experience shows that that approach inevitably smacks of "Trust us! Hear what our experts are telling you". This is usually doomed to failure from the outset.

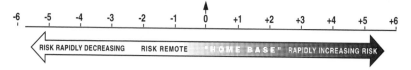

THE PALING PERSPECTIVE SCALE

Company experts are automatically suspect since they are not viewed as independent. To make matters worse, the community is left feeling that there is no way they can get a handle on complicated issues like assessing relative risks. We believe that the seductive simplicity and the evident neutrality of the basic scale can alter this negative scenario.

Credibility and respect are enormously increased if a business feels so confident in their position that they are willing to give blank scales (page 124) to their communities along with help (possibly a grant) to allow the community to get their own assessments of the risk in question from outside sources and put them on the scale for themselves *along with other risks that occur for citizens in that community.*

Despite its limitations, the scale has proved itself to be a valuable tool for business communicators. It helps them achieve one of their most crucial goals, namely to persuade the public to talk about relative risks and then put specific industry concerns into perspective.

Furthermore, the scale has proven to have great appeal to sections of the media and the general public who now recognize that risks can be compared and that reporters should be expected to try to answer "How *relatively* risky do the experts assess this new issue to be and how does it compare to the many other real risks in daily life?"

# FIG. 10 RISK FACTORS on THE PALING PERSPECTIVE SCALE℠

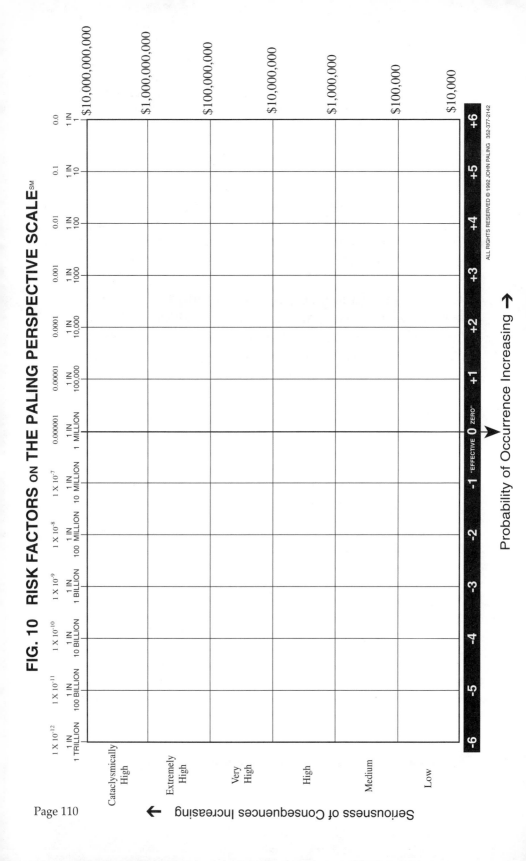

Page 110

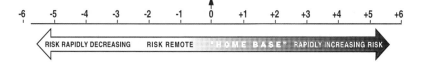

RISK RAPIDLY DECREASING     RISK REMOTE     [RISK INCREASE]     RAPIDLY INCREASING RISK

# What Enquiring Business Minds Want to Know!

For businesses' internal use, the basic Paling Perspective Scale℠ is not enough. For more accurate understanding of risks by corporations, it is necessary to recognize that the potential importance of a particular risk is really a combination of not just one but two factors. Each risk is really the combination of the **probability or likelihood** of a particular risk occurring multiplied by the **seriousness of the consequences** of the event in question. (We clearly acknowledge that limitation to our basic scale back on page 21).

We take the chart to a new level when we recognize that a really big risk only occurs when something very, very serious is also very, very likely to occur. To take this into account, we now offer a two dimensional scale combining both probability and consequences.

The level of probability on the scale is already represented by the numbers on the horizontal axis. Thus the top line proceeds from 1 in 1 ( a factor of 1 or $1 \times 10^0$); to 1 in 10 (a factor of 0.1 or $1 \times 10^{-1}$) ; then to 1 in 100 ( a factor of 0.01 or $1 \times 10^{-2}$) and so on down to one in a trillion $(1 \times 10^{-12})$.

So with a clear understanding of the horizontal axis, it is simple to add the estimated magnitude of the consequences of each risk along the vertical axis of the scale. When this is done, it results in a range of quadrants reflecting different Risk Factors (see Fig. 10, page 110).

THE PALING PERSPECTIVE SCALE

RISK RAPIDLY DECREASING    RISK REMOTE    HOME BASE    RAPIDLY INCREASING RISK

# How to Estimate Consequences

There are several possible ways to chart the seriousness of different risks. For simplicity, we will offer only two.

The first method depends heavily on management's subjective assessment and involves setting arbitrary categories. For example, on the left hand axis of Fig.10, the top row might be considered to represent "Cataclysmically High" consequences and then go down through "Extremely High", "Very High", "High", "Medium" and finally relatively "Low" levels of seriousness at the bottom. (These descriptive categories can be altered to most appropriately cover the range of risks being considered).

Although this attempt to distinguish different levels of severity is somewhat subjective, it is better than nothing. It allows the importance of different risks to be displayed in a grid for comparative purposes and so aids in decision making.

The second method of distinguishing different levels of seriousness is undoubtedly the most persuasive in a business setting and can be summed up in one word: Money.

In most cases this is not "just businesses being heartless" as some skeptics inevitably will suggest. Sadly perhaps, (but inevitably in most public policy issues) it turns out that dollars are the most practicable units for comparing different consequences over many different scenarios.

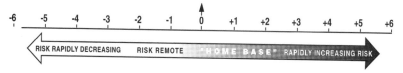

In our litigious American Society, the consequences of a business having a serious accident readily shows up as dollars paid by way of compensation, penalties or out of court settlements to consumers, community members or employees. Additionally, the consequences of business failures or shortcomings may also be reflected in the loss of share value or good will as outside forces respond to an apparent disaster or the way the company handles it.

So pragmatically, business executives can do no better than to assess the consequences of health and safety risks as well as regulated environmental issues by defining the possible damages and then converting the different outcomes to estimates of cost.

For my many environmental friends, let me readily acknowledge that there are important societal and environmental values that can be put at risk by business operations and that, currently, many of these are difficult, if not impossible, to quantify in dollar terms.

Because I have spent most of my life around nature, I personally am very sensitive to this. Indeed, if someone comes up with an alternative, practical unit for assessing all possible different consequences of business risks, then I am certainly willing to add it to the scale.

(In passing, it is worth noting that we all literally buy in to the reality of equating different levels of losses with different levels of money when we purchase a health or life

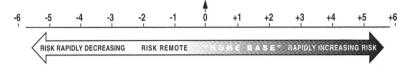

insurance policy. What's more, respected social and environmental organizations also follow the same practice as they estimate the level of importance of an issue and then allocate their resources accordingly).

Undoubtedly the range and numbers of risks for businesses will continue to multiply in parallel with the rapid changes occurring throughout society. That is why this rapid approach to risk assessment using a simple combination of likelihood and seriousness is so valuable. Using Risk Factors provides a way for businesses to decide how much of their limited time and resources they should devote to protecting against different hazards.

## How to Put a Risk Factor to a Business Risk

Let us step back and first look at how businesses can identify what risks they should proactively focus on. Large businesses of course already employ risk managers who are experienced in defining the likely *areas of risk* as well as assessing the possible *costs* if accidents were to happen and the *odds* (the likelihood) of the different scenarios happening.

Smaller companies can do this for themselves by first coming up with a list of serious hazards or potential accidents that might relate to their own circumstances. If a company has never done this before, management can get a good start by tapping into the accumulated experience of their business or trade associations.

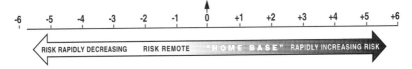

The next step is to review the many different adverse consequences that may result from something going wrong. Take for example, the different consequences of a business accident involving hazardous materials. The possible consequences of a fire, explosion or toxic release would each be reviewed under separate headings like injuries in the community, injuries to workers, damage to property, costs of law suits and business interruption and so on.

By totalling all these possible costs for each of the scenario, you come up with a sum that reflects the total dollar consequences of each risk. These figures would be plotted on the vertical axis of the Risk Factors version of the scale along with the probability estimate that would be shown along the original horizontal axis.

## How Serious Can It Be?

On The Risk Factor version of the scale (page 110), we show a range of costs extending from ten thousand to ten billion dollars. This has been designed to cover the costs for any risk that most companies will ever be exposed to. However, the scale can readily be adapted to guide decision making for larger or smaller entities by adjusting the range of dollars that best reflect the circumstances of the user.

**THE PALING PERSPECTIVE SCALE**

(Showing money along the right hand side of the scale dramatically brings home the reality of how logarithmic scales work. The further the distance from the base line, the more enormous the sums (and the risks) become. Anyone contemplating the possible loss of $100,000 would certainly be concerned: But a loss of $1,000,000 is obviously far larger. Yet there is the same space on the chart between the 10,000 and $100,000 as there is between $100,000 and $1,000,000. In the first case the gap between the two points represents $90,000 but the same gap actually represents $900,000 in the second case!)

The message should be clear. The higher up on the vertical consequences axis a point falls, it gets *disproportionately* serious. In just the same way, the further towards +6 on the bottom line (probability axis) a point falls, the risk becomes *disproportionately* more likely.

Putting these together means that if businesses do go to the trouble of assessing the Risk Factors for different possible scenarios, then they will be well advised to take very seriously all those risks that show up with the highest numbers. What's more, it is likely that this process will bring to light risks that had previously not been viewed as important as they potentially are.

It turns out that there are several major advantages of using this two dimensional Risk Factor approach.

THE PALING PERSPECTIVE SCALE

✓ It significantly reduces the influence of opinion and speculation on what are the biggest risks to a company.

✓ It also makes a strong case for how a company's capital might best be invested to provide maximum protection of the company's assets

✓ It makes a strong case for how a company's capital might best be allocated to produce optimal protection for the health and safety of all concerned.

## Single Number Risk Factors

Before we move on to explain how we simplify the cumbersome numbers that result from multiplying the probabilities with a factor for the consequences, we suggest making one minor adjustment.

Experience shows that if some adverse incident does occur, it is highly unlikely that every one of the possible bad consequences will happen. Think about a house fire for example. Although the property may be insured for the total cost, the reality is that most likely the damage will be less than half of that. On this basis, when working out risk factors, we recommend figuring out the estimate of the maximum cost if all possible things went wrong for a particular risk - and halving it! This gives a more realistic assessment of the costs that would be incurred.

# FIG 11. RISK FACTORS on THE PALING PERSPECTIVE SCALE [SM]

$= \text{Log}_{10}(\frac{1}{2} \text{ Max. Consequences X Max. Probability})$

| | $1,000,000 | | |
|---|---|---|---|
| 3 | 4 | 5 | 6 |
| $\text{Log}_{10}$ of 500,000 X 0.001 = 2.7 | $\text{Log}_{10}$ of 500,000 X 0.01 = 3.7 | $\text{Log}_{10}$ of 500,000 X 0.1 = 4.7 | $\text{Log}_{10}$ of 500,000 X 1 = 5.7 |

$100,000

| 2 | 3 | 4 | 5 |
|---|---|---|---|
| $\text{Log}_{10}$ of 50,000 X 0.001 = 1.7 | $\text{Log}_{10}$ of 50,000 X 0.01 = 2.7 | $\text{Log}_{10}$ of 50,000 X 0.1 = 3.7 | $\text{Log}_{10}$ of 50,000 X 1 = 4.7 |

$10,000

← Seriousness of Consequences Increasing

+2    +3    +4    +5    +6

When you multiply this new cost consequences factor with the probability figure, the resulting number will still be large but there is a quick way to compress it down to a single digit. Since the chart is basically a logarithmic scale, it is a simple matter to use a calculator to work out what mathematicians call the Log of the number. This method is clearly shown on Fig. 11 (page 118). The outcome is an elegant set of simple Risk Factor Numbers.

So the basic formula for a particular Risk Factor on our scale = $Log_{10}$ (½Maximum Consequences Figure X Maximum Probability Figure.) In other words, you would multiply half your figure for the maximum potential seriousness by your estimate for the maximum probability. (If you have an estimate of the *actual* instead of the maximum *potential* cost of the consequences, it is appropriate to use that figure without halving it) Take the final number and enter it into a scientific calculator and simply tap the $Log_{10}$ function key.

The resulting Risk Factor number is a valuable and realistic appraisal for businesses of the true potential magnitude of particular risks. If the estimates used are realistic, Risk Factors can provide a powerful tool for management to make better business decisions and to move closer to every manager's dream of "No Surprises".

# FIG. 12 RISK FACTORS on The Paling Perspective Scale℠

| | $1 \times 10^{-12}$ | $1 \times 10^{-11}$ | $1 \times 10^{-10}$ | $1 \times 10^{-9}$ | $1 \times 10^{-8}$ | $1 \times 10^{-7}$ | 0.000001 | 0.00001 | 0.0001 | 0.001 | 0.01 | 0.1 | 0.0 | |
| | 1 IN 1 TRILLION | 1 IN 100 BILLION | 1 IN 10 BILLION | 1 IN 1 BILLION | 1 IN 100 MILLION | 1 IN 10 MILLION | 1 IN 1 MILLION | 1 IN 100,000 | 1 IN 10,000 | 1 IN 1000 | 1 IN 100 | 1 IN 10 | 1 IN 1 | |
| A | -1 | 0 | 1 | 2 | 3 | 4 | 5 | 6 | 7 | 8 | 9 | 10 | | $10,000,000,000 |
| B | -2 | -1 | 0 | 1 | 2 | 3 | 4 | 5 | 6 | 7 | 8 | 9 | | $1,000,000,000 |
| C | -3 | -2 | -1 | 0 | 1 | 2 | 3 | 4 | 5 | 6 | 7 | 8 | | $100,000,000 |
| D | -4 | -3 | -2 | -1 | 0 | 1 | 2 | 3 | 4 | 5 | 6 | 7 | | $10,000,000 |
| E | -5 | -4 | -3 | -2 | -1 | 0 | 1 | 2 | 3 | 4 | 5 | 6 | | $1,000,000 |
| F | -6 | -5 | -4 | -3 | -2 | -1 | 0 | 1 | 2 | 3 | 4 | 5 | | $100,000 |
| | -6 | -5 | -4 | -3 | -2 | -1 | "EFFECTIVE 0 ZERO" | +1 | +2 | +3 | +4 | +5 | +6 | $10,000 |

← Seriousness of Consequences Increasing

Probability of Occurrence Increasing →

Most important of all, using Risk Factors should increase the safety performance of every company by focusing most of the available resources on what have been determined to be the most serious risks. This should be acknowledged by those who feel uncomfortable with businesses using a financial measure for allocating resources on different risks that may be societal or environmental.

Risk Factors make it easier for health, safety and environment professionals to make their case to top management for what needs to be done and where capital should be allocated. Recommendations that result from such a quantitative analysis fit easily into the business decision making process and thus are easier to sell.

More often than not, going through the steps of identifying Risk Factors generates ideas on how to mitigate possible disasters. Having identified the largest potential risks, it is often possible to take actions to mitigate the possible costs by focusing on reducing the probability or the consequences in some way. This approach can result in significant reduction of risk with very little additional expenditure of capital.

In Fig.12 (page 120), we have shown the Risk Factors to the nearest whole number. However, for real life situations, we recommend expressing the numbers as decimals to counteract the way the scale compresses differences and to show important distinctions that would otherwise be lumped together within the same block.

THE PALING PERSPECTIVE SCALE

| -6 | -5 | -4 | -3 | -2 | -1 | 0 | +1 | +2 | +3 | +4 | +5 | +6 |

RISK RAPIDLY DECREASING   RISK REMOTE   RAPIDLY INCREASING RISK

# Getting The Most From Risk Factors

Undoubtedly, this Risk Factor approach is most useful for assessing environmental and occupational health & safety risks associated with existing industrial processes and for factoring in the significance of human errors as components of accidents and failures. It is also useful in comparing transportation alternatives and in the design and planning of whole new operations.

Additionally, it is a good tool for assessing risks for insurance considerations. (Notice however that a given Risk Factor number may represent an insignificant burden for one company yet totally overwhelm another, depending on the particular company's economic resilience.)

Having laid out some of the benefits of Risk Factors for corporations, I must again admit that some business risks cannot be plotted on the scale as yet. Pivotal business decisions like appointing key executives, deciding how much debt to assume, whether to expand into new markets or deciding which new business enterprises to pursue, all these present significant risks that currently cannot be fully assessed by the Risk Factor approach.

In areas like these, management has to fall back on personal experience backed by good old intuition – not a bad combination after all since it has served top executives well over the years.

| -6 | -5 | -4 | -3 | -2 | -1 EFFECTIVE | 0 ZERO | +1 | +2 | +3 | +4 | +5 | +6 |

## THE PALING PERSPECTIVE SCALE

| -6 | -5 | -4 | -3 | -2 | -1 | 0 | +1 | +2 | +3 | +4 | +5 | +6 |

RISK RAPIDLY DECREASING     RISK REMOTE     HOME BASE     RAPIDLY INCREASING RISK

# In Summary

In view of the fact that modern corporate life can have major downturns as well as up sides, we recommend that our clients put some time into examining the most vulnerable aspects of running their business. Whenever estimates of probability and consequences can be factored together and compared with other issues competing for resources and protective strategies, Risk Factors on The Paling Perspective Scale[SM] can provide valuable perspectives for better management decisions.

*We hope this reduces the feeling of being
Up To Your Armpits in Alligators!*

| -6 | -5 | -4 | -3 | -2 | -1 EFFECTIVE 0 ZERO | +1 | +2 | +3 | +4 | +5 | +6 |

THE PALING PERSPECTIVE SCALE℠ from the book "Up To Your Armpits in Alligators?" © JOHN PALING 1992 ☎ 352 377 2142

| -6 | -5 | -4 | -3 | -2 | -1 | 0 | +1 | +2 | +3 | +4 | +5 | +6 |
|---|---|---|---|---|---|---|---|---|---|---|---|---|
| 1 IN 1,000,000 MILLION | 1 IN 100,000 MILLION | 1 IN 10,000 MILLION | 1 IN 1,000 MILLION | 1 IN 100 MILLION | 1 IN 10 MILLION | 1 IN 1 MILLION | 1 IN 100,000 | 1 IN 10,000 | 1 IN 1000 | 1 IN 100 | 1 IN 10 | 1 IN 1 |
| 0.00001 IN A MILLION | 0.0001 IN A MILLION | 0.0001 IN A MILLION | 0.001 IN A MILLION | 0.01 IN A MILLION | 0.1 IN A MILLION | IN A MILLION | 10 IN A MILLION | 100 IN A MILLION | 1,000 IN A MILLION | 10,000 IN A MILLION | 100,000 IN A MILLION | 1,000,000 IN A MILLION |
| $1 \times 10^{-12}$ | $1 \times 10^{-11}$ | $1 \times 10^{-10}$ | $1 \times 10^{-9}$ | $1 \times 10^{-8}$ | $1 \times 10^{-7}$ | $1 \times 10^{-6}$ | $1 \times 10^{-5}$ | $1 \times 10^{-4}$ | $1 \times 10^{-3}$ | $1 \times 10^{-2}$ | $1 \times 10^{-1}$ | $1 \times 10^{0}$ |

RISK MASSIVE

RAPIDLY INCREASING RISK

HOME "BASE"

RISK REMOTE

RISK RAPIDLY DECREASING

MINUSCULE RISK

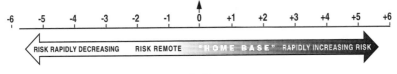

THE PALING PERSPECTIVE SCALE

# -14 -

# RESOURCES FOR BETTER UNDERSTANDING RELATIVE RISKS

To help readers further their understanding of relative risks, we are including some references to other people's writings. We also have provided a blank chart (page 124) that readers may wish to copy and use for plotting risks for themselves.

Permisssion is granted to reproduce and distribute this chart (with the full copyright notice visible) for educational and not for profit purposes. Use of any of the materials in this book in a compilation to be sold or distributed for profit, requires written agreement from the publisher.

## Recommended Books for Non-Technical Readers

**Responding to Community Outrage: Strategies for Effective Risk Commuication** by Peter M. Sandman 1993 Published by the American Industrial Hygiene Association. ISBN 0-932627-51-X (Contact: 2700 Prosperity Avenue, Fairfax, VA 22031 Phone 202/ 833 2184)

*For those seeking an understanding of why the public is often frightened by risks that the experts truly consider to be tiny and how citizens' level of response to "Risk" is typically a reflection of "Hazard + Outrage". This is an easy to understand summary of many years of experience and research.*

## Reporting on Risk: A Handbook for Journalists and Citizens by Michael Kamrin, Dolores Katz and Martha Walter 1995 Published by Michigan Sea Grant & The Foundation for American Communications. ISBN 1-885756-08-9 (Contact: 2200 Bonisteel Boulevard, Ann Arbor, MI 48109 - Phone 313/ 764 1138)

*For those seeking an understanding of how scientists set about measuring risks and how "the experts" compile the sorts of figures that are quoted in our charts. This small book explains some of the unspoken assumptions and the uncertainties that are often inevitable when authorities try to produce good estimates of risks and to define "safety factors".*

## Beating Murphy's Law: the Amazing Science of Risk.
By Bob Berger 1994 Published by Dell Publishing. ISBN 0-385-31317-9. (Contact: Bantam, Doubleday Dell Publishing Group, Inc 1540 Broadway, New York, New York 10036.)

*This is a painless way of learning the ins and outs of risk assessment. It reads as a witty and entertaining story about real life situations as the author meets and gets to know his wife while assessing the odds of most of the day-to-day events that happen along the way. This book is so much fun that you don't realize how much you are learning.*

## Chemicals, the Press, and the Public: A Journalist's Guide to Reporting on Chemicals in the Community. By Bud Ward. Published by Environmental Health Council, (Contact: National Safety Council, 1050 17th Street, N.W., Suite 770,Washington, DC 20036   Phone 202/293 2270)

*This book provides both background on chemical risks and an extensive list of information sources.*

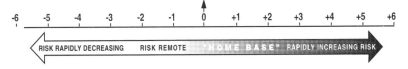

# Sources For The Odds
# Of Different Risks

People in North America are in some ways very lucky. The Freedom of Information Act has fueled citizens' expectations that they have "a right to know" and this has resulted in access to a wide range of official statistics. Thus, in theory, it should be easy for U.S. citizens to get their hands on the odds for risks they are interested in so they can put them into perspective on one of our charts.

However, the reality is that the most readily available figures often do not take you very far! The sorts of statistics that the government agencies collect and publish seem to be focused more on numbers that the politicians are interested in and less on what the general public would most like to know!

For example, I do not know of a simple account of the odds for the hundreds of real and remote risks that The Average Joe, The Typical Jessie and the Regular Roberto Family experience annually in the U.S.A. These figures would give everyone a broad background level for the many "risks with which we all are at home" so that citizens and the media could put new, potentially worrisome risks into better perspective.

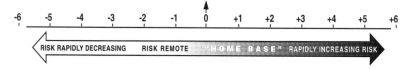

THE PALING PERSPECTIVE SCALE

Finding believable figures takes more time and effort than you might expect. It turns out that to get figures for a particular risk, you probably will have to contact the government or state agency most likely to be involved and then follow the leads that emerge from there. It is also valuable to ask for figures from related business associations and also from their political opponents.

Here are a few valuable sources for obtaining the statistics for the odds of different risks in the U.S.A.

**Statistical Abstract of the United States: The National Data Book.** Published annually by U.S. Department of Commerce, Economics and Statistics Administration, Bureau of the Census. Washington DC. (Available in Reference section of many libraries or Phone 301/763 5299) Also http://www.census.gov

**National Center for Health Statistics: Data Dissemination Branch.** 6525 Belcrest Road, Room 10674, Hyattsville, MD 20782 Phone 301/436 8500. Also http://www.cdc.gov/nchswww/nchshome.htm

**Accident Facts** 1996 Edition Published by the National Safety Council ISBN 0-87912-183-1 (Contact: NSC at 1121 Spring Lake Drive, Itasca, IL 60143 Phone 1 800-621-7619)

# ACKNOWLEDGEMENTS

Many people have given us their assistance and encouragement on a personal basis during the course of working on this project. Since we have tried to use resources from different sides of certain risk issues, the expression of our gratitude to some of these people here does not imply their agreement to the final contents of the book.

In particular, we thank **Chris Borgert, Ray Harbison, Stephen Price, Deborah Ardizzona, Brian O'Hara, Bridget Woodman, Harold Hicks, Chuck Mlakar, Brian Duperreault, William Dondarski and Bob Elliott.**

Significant assistance for editorial, design and layout services was provided by **Linda and Bob Dunn, Rick Q. Chin, Amy E. Schaumann and Christine Gonzalez**.

Additional graphics help was provided by **Mick Magnusson, Katherine Momberger and Elizabeth Nason.**

Original alligator illustrations were provided by **May Cheney** and the cartoons in the charts were specially produced by **Don Baumgart**.

Any errors are the work of **The Devil, Environmental Extremists** or **Lying Industrialists**, depending on the reader's emotional perspective of relative risk!

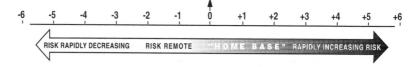

# SOURCES FOR THE FIGURES BEHIND THE POINTS ON THE SCALES

**Fig. 1 - THE BASIC SCALE.** This is the basic matrix before any points have been added.

**Fig. 2 - RISKS WITH WHICH WE ARE "AT HOME"**

(1)• **Risk of drowning in tub this year = $1.5 \times 10^{-6}$**
Source: Les Krantz, What The Odds Are, 1992, pg. 292. Harper Perennial. ISBN: 0-06-271521. "You will drown in the tub this year 1 chance in 685,000."
Annual risk = $1/6.85 \times 10^5 = 1 \times 10^{-5}/6.85 = 0.15 \times 0^{-5} = 1.5 \times 10^{-6}$.

(2)• **Risk of resident being struck by a crashing airplane = $4 \times 10^{-6}$.**
Source: Harvard Center of Risk Analysis, 1992 Annual Report, pg. 3.
Harvard School of Public Health: "Involuntary risks of death in U.S.A. Resident struck on the ground by crashing airplane p. =.000004" = $4 \times 10^{-6}$.

(3)• **Risk of mother dying in single childbirth = $6.6 \times 10^{-5}$.**
Source: Harvard School of Public Health, Center for Risk Analysis, 1992 Annual Report pg. 3. "Involuntary risks of death in the U.S. Woman dies in childbirth (2 children)" "p = .000122" = $1.22 \times 10^{-4}$ "Risk per child" = $0.66 \times 10^{-4} = 6.6 \times 10^{-5}$

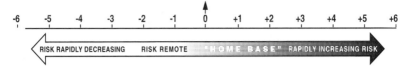

(4)• **Risk of being struck by lightning = 1.1 X 10⁻⁴**
Source: Les Krantz, <u>What The Odds Are</u>, 1992, pg. 292.
Harper. ISBN: 0-06-271521.
Risk of being struck by lightning "1 in 9,100" = $1/9.1 \times 10^3$
$= 1 \times 10^{-3}/9.1 = 0.11 \times 10^{-3} = 1.1 \times 10^{-4}$.

(5)• **Death from home accidents per year = 1.1 X 10⁻⁴**
Source: Wilson & Crouch, <u>Science</u>, Vol. 236, 1987, pg. 236.
Annual risk = $1.1 \times 10^{-4}$."
(Editorial makes clear that the figures quoted are for "annual
risk of death.")

(6)• **Extra incidents of death from cancer from drinking one
light beer per day for one year = 2 X 10⁻⁵**
Source: Wilson, R., 1980, <u>Risk/Benefit Analysis for Toxic
Chemicals</u>; "Ecotoxicology and Environmental Safety" Vol.
4, pg. 370-383.
Annual risk = $2 \times 10^{-5}$ or 20 in a million per year each year.

(7)• **Extra chance of death from cancer from living in Denver
compared to living in New York for one year = 1 X 10⁻⁵**
Source: Wilson, R., 1980, <u>Risk/Benefit Analysis for Toxic
Chemicals</u>; "Ecotoxicology and Environmental Safety" Vol.
4, pg. 370-383.
Annual risk = $1 \times 10^{-5}$.

(8)• **Extra risk of death from cancer from eating peanut butter
sandwich per day for a year = 1 X 10⁻⁵ represents a "+1" on
our scale**
Source: Wilson, R., 1980, <u>Risk/Benefit Analysis for Toxic
Chemicals</u>; "Ecotoxicology and Environmental Safety" Vol.
4, pg. 370-383. "$4 \times 10^{-5}$ is yearly risk for 4 tablespoons full
of peanut butter per day."
Annual risk = $1 \times 10^{-5}$.

| -6 | -5 | -4 | -3 | -2 | -1 EFFECTIVE | 0 ZERO | +1 | +2 | +3 | +4 | +5 | +6 |
|----|----|----|----|----|-----|-----|----|----|----|----|----|----|

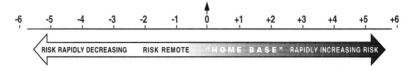

**THE PALING PERSPECTIVE SCALE**

(9)• **Extra incidents of cancer from eating $^1/_2$ lb. of charcoal broiled steak once a week for one year = 4 X $10^{-7}$**
Source: Wilson, R., 1980, <u>Risk/Benefit Analysis for Toxic Chemicals</u>; "Ecotoxicology and Environmental Safety" Vol. 4, pg. 370-383.
Annual risk = 4 X $10^{-7}$.

(10)• **U.S. Food & Drug Administration point below which any risk from a food additive is considered too small to be of concern = 1 X $10^{-6}$**
Source: Wilson & Crouch, <u>Science</u>, Vol. 236, 1987, pg. 293.
Note: The FDA is mandated to prevent food becoming contaminated or adulterated. It has accepted as "safe" the standard that if a food additive (or its breakdown products) increases the chance by less than one cancer per million lifetimes, the threat is considered to be too small to be of concern. (For the purposes of this chart, we are excluding reference to "Delaney Clause" issues relating to carcinogens.)

Fig. 3 - RISKS OF INJURIES AT HOME, associated with consumer products and requiring emergency treatment in U.S.A.
hospitals, 1989.
Source: Statistical Abstract of U.S. 92, U.S. Department of Commerce, BUREAU OF CENSUS. ISBN: 0-16-038080. Paperback: ISBN:
0-16-03801; "Injuries associated with consumer products in 1988 &
1989. Chart No. 185."

- Refrigerators/freezers     $31,630/2.5 \times 10^8 = 1.26 \times 10^{-4}$
- Television sets     $34,949/2.5 \times 10^8 = 1.40 \times 10^{-4}$
- Lawn mowers     $61,864/2.5 \times 10^8 = 2.47 \times 10^{-4}$
- Power home tools     $93,076/2.5 \times 10^8 = 3.72 \times 10^{-4}$
- Bathtubs and showers     $121,600/2.5 \times 10^6 = 4.94 \times 10^{-4}$
- Ladders and stools     $131,551/2.5 \times 10^8 = 5.26 \times 10^{-4}$
- Beds, mattresses, pillows     $302,190/2.5 \times 10^8 = 5.03 \times 10^{-4}$
- Carpets and rugs     $87,738/2.5 \times 10^8 = 3.5 \times 10^{-4}$
- Stairs, ramps, landings, etc.     $1,450,421/2.5 \times 10^8 = 5.8 \times 10^{-3}$
- Nails, carpet tacks, etc.     $214,123/2.5 \times 10^8 = 8.56 \times 10^{-4}$
- Drinking glasses     $114,683/2.5 \times 10^8 = 4.58 \times 10^{-4}$
- Cans, glass bottles, jars     $250,542/2.5 \times 10^8 = 1.0 \times 10^{-3}$
- Exercise equipment     $67,028/2.5 \times 10^8 = 2.68 \times 10^{-4}$
- Toys     $147,898/2.5 \times 10^8 = 5.9 \times 10^{-4}$
- Sinks and toilets     $43,162/2.5 \times 10^8 = 1.7 \times 10^{-4}$

| -6 | -5 | -4 | -3 | -2 | -1 EFFECTIVE 0 ZERO | +1 | +2 | +3 | +4 | +5 | +6 |

THE PALING PERSPECTIVE SCALE

## Fig. 4 - THE GENERAL PERSPECTIVE SCALE

(1)•  **Risk of dying of something finally! 1 in 1**
*This represents a "+6" on our scale*
<u>Source</u>: Common experience - excluding divine interven-
tion or any relationship to Elvis! (This is included to remind
ourselves that there is always going to be some cause of
death for everybody sooner or later.)
Calculated as a chance of 1 in 1; or 1,000,000 in a million.

(2)•  **Risk of cancer being the ultimate cause of death**
**= 2.5 X 10⁻¹**
*This represents a "+5 $1/_5$" on our scale.*
<u>Source</u>: Harvard School of Public Health, Center For Risk
Analysis, <u>1991 Annual Report</u>, pg. 2.
"The average American's lifetime risk of fatal cancer is
about one chance in four."
Estimated as a chance of 1 in 4; or 250,000 in a million
$= 2.5 \times 10^{-1}$.

(3)•  **Risk of death through Russian roulette = 1.67 X 10⁻¹**
*This represents a "+5 $1/_3$" on our scale.*
<u>Source</u>: Simple calculation. One cylinder in six would have
a live bullet which at point blank range would cause death.
Inserted to simply show where such a massive risk shows
up on our scale.
Estimated as a chance of 1 in 6; or 166,666 in a million
$= 1.67 \times 10^{-1}$.

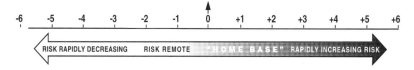

-6  -5  -4  -3  -2  -1  0  +1  +2  +3  +4  +5  +6

RISK RAPIDLY DECREASING     RISK REMOTE     HOME BASE     RAPIDLY INCREASING RISK

(4) • **Risk of dying from cancer - smoking 1 pack a day for 30 years = 1.08 X $10^{-1}$**
*This represents a "+5" on our scale.*
Source: Wilson & Crouch Science, 1987, Vol. 236, pgs. 267 - 268, quoted at "annual risk of 3.6 X $10^{-3}$."

3,600 per million each year, multiplied by a conservative 30 years to give what we show here as "per lifetime." = 108,000 per million or over 10 percent.
Extra chance of death from cancer from smoking one pack of cigarettes a day for a lifetime of 30 years: 30 years X 3.6 X $10^{-3}$ = 1.08 X $10^{-1}$.

(5) • **Highway death from 50 years of driving = 2 X $10^{-4}$"**
*This represents a "+4" on our scale.*
Note TWO sources in conflict:
Source: 1) Wilson & Crouch, Science , 1987, Vol. 236, pg. 241.
"Annual risk of death from driving motor vehicles is 2 X $10^{-4}$."
Thus annual risk is = 2 in 10,000 or 200 in a million per year.
An underline risk of 2 X $10^{-4}$" represents a "+2 $1/4$" on our scale.
Thus for a 50-year lifetime = 100 in a 10,000 or = +4 on our chart.
Source: 2) Harvard School of Public Health, Center For Risk Analysis, Annual Report, 1991, page 11.
"20 in a million highway deaths in USA per year."
Thus annual risk of highway death is 2 X $10^{-5}$ which represents a "+$1^{1/4}$" on our scale.
Thus risk of death during 50-year lifetime =100 X $10^{-5}$ , or 1 X $10^{-3}$ or 1 in 1000 which represents "+ 3" on our scale.
Thus 1000 per million - highway deaths in U.S.A per 50 year lifetime = 1 in 1000 =1 X $10^{-3}$ = +3 on our chart.

-6  -5  -4  -3  -2  -1 EFFECTIVE 0 ZERO  +1  +2  +3  +4  +5  +6

-6  -5  -4  -3  -2  -1  0  +1  +2  +3  +4  +5  +6

RISK RAPIDLY DECREASING    RISK REMOTE    HOME BASE    RAPIDLY INCREASING RISK

(6)• **Risk of death from radon over 60 years = 3.36 X 10⁻³**
*This represents a "+3 ¹/₂" on our scale.*
<u>Source</u>: <u>EPA Chart for Gainesville</u>, quotes, National Safety Council, 1990, "between 7,000 and 30,000 deaths per year." All background information comes from EPA's "A Citizen's Guide to Radon."
Averages to "14,000 deaths per year - across the United States."
Assume population of U.S.A. is 250,000,000.
Then one death = 14,000 divided by 250,000,000 = 5.6 X 10⁻⁵ per year.
*This <u>annual risk</u> is 56 deaths per 1,000,000 per year which represents "+1²/₃" on our scale.*
Or over 60-year lifetime period lifetime = or 3,360 deaths per million = 3.36 X 10⁻³.

(7)• **Risk of dying each yr. from accidents at home = 1.1 X 10⁻⁴**
*This represents a "+2" on our scale.*
<u>Source</u>: Wilson & Crouch, <u>Science</u>, 1987, pg. 236. (Editorial makes clear that the figures quoted are for "<u>annual risk of death</u>.")
"Annual risk = 1.1 X 10⁻⁴" - represents a "+2" on our scale.

(8)• **Risk of mother dying in single childbirth = 6.6 X 10⁻⁵**
*This represents a "+1 ⁷/₈" on our scale.*
<u>Source</u>: Harvard School of Public Health, Center For Risk Analysis, <u>1992 Annual Report</u>, pg. 3. "Involuntary risks of death in U.S.A. Woman dies in childbirth (2 children)" = "000122" = 1.22 X 10⁻⁴.
*This represents a "+2" on our scale.*
"Risk per single child" = 0.66 X 10⁻⁴ = 6.6 X 10⁻⁵ which represents "+1 ⁷/₈" on our scale.

-6  -5  -4  -3  -2  -1 EFFECTIVE 0 ZERO  +1  +2  +3  +4  +5  +6

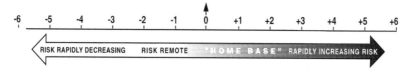

-6  -5  -4  -3  -2  -1  0  +1  +2  +3  +4  +5  +6

RISK RAPIDLY DECREASING    RISK REMOTE    "HOME BASE"    RAPIDLY INCREASING RISK

(9) • **Risk of lung cancer from asbestos in schools = 5 X 10⁻⁶**
*This represents a "+²/₃" on our scale.*
<u>Source</u>: Wilson & Crouch, <u>Science</u>, Vol. 236, pg. 292. Est. "5 per million lifetimes" = 5 X 10⁻⁶.

The probability of children getting lung cancer from such asbestos exposure in school is estimated to be about "5 per million lifetimes" - less than 1/5000 the chance of death faced by these children from other current events in their lives. (Careless removal can pose major risks to the workmen as well as to children - so many experts believe it should be left if it is in good repair and removed only when there is a major renovation.)
Risk of child getting lung cancer from asbestos in schools = 5 X 10⁻⁶.

(10) • <u>**USA EPA regulates so risks fall in or below this range.**</u>
1 X 10⁻³ to 1 X 10⁻⁶. Source: Statement by William K. Reilly, Administrator of U.S. EPA on Environmental Tobacco Smoke, Jan. 7, 1992. "Merely for comparison, EPA generally sets its standards or regulations so that risks are below 1-in-1,000 to 1-in-1 million."

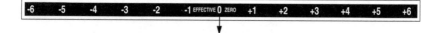

-6  -5  -4  -3  -2  -1 EFFECTIVE 0 ZERO  +1  +2  +3  +4  +5  +6

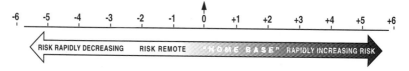

THE PALING PERSPECTIVE SCALE

## Fig. 5 -ANNUAL RISKS ASSOCIATED WITH SIZEWELL A NUCLEAR STATION

(1) • Maximum risk from drinking milk from local farms $5 \times 10^{-8}$
(2) • Maximum risk to eaters of local vegetables $5 \times 10^{-8}$
(3) • Maximum risk to eaters of local shellfish $2.6 \times 10^{-7}$
(4) • Maximum risk from exposure on coastline $5 \times 10^{-7}$
(5) • Maximum risk form airborne radiation $1.7 \times 10^{-6}$
(6) • Maximum risk from exposure to near perimeter fence $2.6 \times 10^{-6}$
(7) • Risk due to all possible nuclear accidents $1 \times 10^{-6}$
(8) • Worst case total risk from normal operation + nuclear accidents $6.1 \times 10^{-6}$
(9) • Legal maximum man-made risk to public $5 \times 10^{-5}$
(10) • Maximum tolerable risk to radiation worker permitted by industry $8.0 \times 10^{-4}$
(11) • Average risk to nuclear power station worker $4.0 \times 10^{-5}$
(12) • Average risk to public from natural radiation $1.1 \times 10^{-4}$
(13) • Range of risk to public from natural radiation $5 \times 10^{-5}$ to $5 \times 10^{-3}$

See also Pages 140 -145

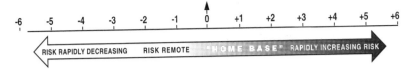

# THE PALING PERSPECTIVE SCALE

## Fig 6. - LIFETIME RISKS ASSOCIATED WITH SIZEWELL A NUCLEAR STATION

(1) • Maximum risk from drinking milk from local farms $3.5 \times 10^{-6}$
(2) • Maximum risk to eaters of local vegetable $3.5 \times 10^{-6}$
(3) • Maximum risk to eaters of local shellfish $1.8 \times 10^{-5}$
(4) • Maximum risk from exposure on coastline $3.5 \times 10^{-5}$
(5) • Maximum risk from airborne radiation $1.2 \times 10^{-4}$
(6) • Maximum risk from exposure to near perimeter fence $1.8 \times 10^{-4}$
(7) • Risk due to all possible nuclear accidents $7.0 \times 10^{-5}$
(8) • Worst case total risk from normal operation + nuclear accidents $4.3 \times 10^{-4}$
(9) • Legal maximum man-made risk to public $3.5 \times 10^{-3}$
(10) • Maximum tolerable risk to radiation worker permitted by industry $3.2 \times 10^{-2}$
(11) • Average risk to nuclear power station worker $1.6 \times 10^{-3}$
(12) • Average risk to public from natural radiation $7.7 \times 10^{-3}$
(13) • Range of risk to public from natural radiation $3.5 \times 10^{-3}$ to $3.5 \times 10^{-1}$

See also Pages 140 -145

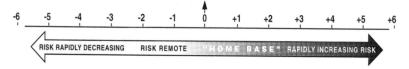
# BACKGROUND TO CALCULATING THE NUCLEAR RISKS SUMMARIZED IN FIGS 5 & 6

Sizewell Nuclear Power Station is situated on the southeast coast of England and is operated by Nuclear Electric plc. The facility operates 2 Magnox reactors with steel pressure vessels and air-shield cooling. We chose "Sizewell A" (there is also a "Sizewell B") as the site to demonstrate the functioning of The Paling Perspective Scale[SM] simply because of the availability of detailed and up to date environmental monitoring data. At the same time, because the whole topic of nuclear generation has been continually criticized over the years by anti-nuclear groups, we anticipated that we would obtain very different perspectives of the risks involved.

Our goal was to get both the nuclear industry and the anti-nuclear groups to spell out for us their estimates of the risks to the general public and the workers of the plant. We hoped to put those two positions into perspective on our chart and compare these assessments of risk to our Home Base Zone. We wanted to make it possible for a non technical observer to get a feel for the levels of disagreement between the two groups and, more important, to put the risks from a nuclear generator into perspective with the risks that we are all at home with.

As we explain on pages 68 - 71, our friends from Greenpeace and other anti-nuclear groups chose not to explain their opposition on the grounds of specific levels of risk so our charts reflect data only from official figures published by England's National Radiation Protection Board (NRPB,) the International Commission of Radiation Protection (ICRP) and the Health and Safety Executive (HSE). The points shown on our charts represent the "upper bound" estimates of *maximum* doses of radiation to the local population from Sizewell A during 1991.

# Data Points and Sources for Sizewell A

The following figures are based on the results of environmental monitoring of the Sizewell site during 1991 and the corresponding estimates of the maximum annual doses received by the public from all significant pathways (Ref. A). However, as presented, the technical data are not expressed in a form that makes it possible for the public to understand the levels of relative risk that are involved. Thus our first task was to convert these figures into units that can be positioned on The Paling Perspective Scale.

### Conversion From Dose Received To Annual Risk

In order to convert any dose received figure into a level of risk to human life, a 'risk/Sievert' conversion factor is required. (A Seivert (Sv) is a unit for expressing radiation dose levels.)

The conversion factor used for all figures presented concerning members of the public is $5 \times 10^{-2}$ Sv$^{-1}$ and concerning radiation workers is $4 \times 10^{-2}$ Sv$^{-1}$. These figures, meaning the risk of death for every Sievert accumulated during a lifetime, are the most recent estimate published by the ICRP (Ref. B). In all cases, the figure of yearly dose received in Sieverts is multiplied by the appropriate conversion factor to obtain the estimate of the annual risk associated with that dose.

The use of a single conversion factor may be unsuitable for evaluating risks due to radiation when there is a large variation in the rates at which the radiation doses are received. For the risk calculation for Sizewell however, a single conversion factor is appropriate as the quoted dose rates are all below 100 mSv per annum and are assumed to be received uniformly throughout the year.

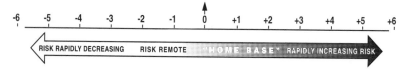

## Conversion From Annual To Lifetime Risk

For the purpose of effective communication of risk and comparison with other risks in life, we have quoted the data for Sizewell as lifetime as well as annual risks. Lifetime risks were estimated by calculating the accumulation of the estimated annual risks associated with a given source of radiation over the average number of years an individual is likely to be exposed to these emissions. In most of the calculations presented here, the length of exposure is taken to be 70 years, approximating the average human lifetime.

In fairness, it must be pointed out that this method gives an overly pessimistic impression. It is unrealistic to believe that any member of the public will always live in the same area and be exposed to the same maximum risk levels from every possible source throughout their lives. Thus the risk levels we show will consequently be somewhat higher than anything experienced in reality. However for maximum public confidence, we have shown the maximum risk estimates in each case.

The lifetime risk can be calculated simply by multiplying the yearly risk by the average number of years of exposure. This is just an approximation but with the risk levels and exposure lengths relevant to Sizewell, it results in a loss of acuracy of less than 1%. For example here is more detailed information behind the summaries shown in Fig 6.

| Pathway | Maximum Lifetime Risk |
|---|---|
| **(1) Milk Contamination** (Mainly $S^{35}$ and $C^{14}$) Max yearly dose = 1 μSv | $3.5 \times 10^{-6}$ |
| **(2) Vegetation Contamination** (Mainly $S^{35}$ and $C^{14}$) Max yearly dose = 1 μSv | $3.5 \times 10^{-6}$ |

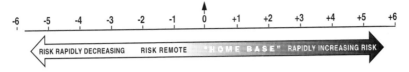

## THE PALING PERSPECTIVE SCALE

RISK RAPIDLY DECREASING    RISK REMOTE    "HOME BASE"    RAPIDLY INCREASING RISK

(3) **Seafood Contamination**
(Various )                                    $1.8 \times 10^{-5}$
Max yearly dose = 5 µSv

(4) **Beach Activity**
(Proximity to coolant outlets)                $3.5 \times 10^{-5}$
Max yearly dose = 10 µSv

(5) **Airborne Discharges**
(Mainly $Ar^{41}$ from air cooling)           $1.2 \times 10^{-4}$
Max yearly dose = 35 µSv

(6) **Direct irradiation**
(Unattenuated by shielding)                   $1.8 \times 10^{-4}$
Max yearly dose = 50 µSv

7) In order to be licensed to operate a nuclear power station in the UK, calculations must be produced to show the overall risk of death to members of the public from all possible of nuclear accidents is less than $1 \times 10^{-4}$ per year, and as far as is reasonably practicable, below $1 \times 10^{-6}$ (Ref. C). Nuclear Electric is presently working to demonstrate that accidental risks associated with their power stations conform to these new requirements as part of their 'long term safety review.' In anticipation of the results of their calculations for Sizewell A, the limit of $1 \times 10^{-6}$ per year is used for the estimation of lifetime risk to the public from nuclear accidents.

**Nuclear Accident** (All possibilities)        $7 \times 10^{-5}$

(8) Summing all of these risks gives the absolute worst case total lifetime risk of any member of the public due to the Sizewell A. This absolute maximum risk level is not representative of

the actual risk to any group of the local population but is included as an upper limit for comparison with more general data points.

**Worst Case Total Risk From Sizewell**     $4.3 \times 10^{-4}$

# Data Points for General Radiation Risks

For comparison with the risks due to Sizewell, more general risk levels associated with exposure to radiation in the UK are presented.

(9)  The HSE on recommendation from the ICRP specify a maximum dose to the public from any single source of man- made radiation in the UK of 1 mSv per year (Ref's A & C). The corresponding maximum tolerable lifetime risk is calculated assuming an average length of exposure of 70 years.

**Legal maximum risk to UK public from man-made radiation source:     $3.5 \times 10^{-3}$**

(10) & (11)  For workers at nuclear power stations, the ICRP recommended the maximum tolerable dose from exposure at work is 20 mSv per year (Ref.'s B & C). In practice tight safety controls are used to ensure dose levels are kept as low as reasonably achievable, the average level of exposure being 1 mSv per year (Ref. C). Assuming a length of exposure of 40 working years, the following lifetime risks are calculated.

**Maximum tolerable risk to long serving radiation worker: $3.2 \times 10^{-2}$**   (Point 10)

**Average risk to long serving radiation worker at a nuclear power station:  $1.6 \times 10^{-3}$** (Point 11)

# THE PALING PERSPECTIVE SCALE

(12) & (13)   The radiation doses received by individual members of the public in the UK from natural sources of radiation range from 1 mSv to 100 mSv per year (Ref.'s A & D) with an average of 2.2 mSv (Ref. D). Using these figures and assuming an average length of exposure of 70 years, the lifetime risks are calculated.

**Range of risks from natural radiation: 3.5 X $10^{-3}$ to 3.5 X $10^{-1}$** (Point 12)

**Average risk from natural radiation: 7.7 X $10^{-3}$ (Point 13)**

## References:

(A) 'Report on Radioactive Discharges and Environmental Monitoring During 1991.' Nuclear Electric plc publication. HSD/ OSB/R/004.

(B) 'ICRP 60.' International Commission on Radiation Protection publication. ISBN: 0/08041144/4.

(C) 'Tolerability of Risk.' Health and Safety Executive (HSE) publication. ISBN: 0/11/886368/1.

(D) 'Living With Radiation.' National Radiation Protection Board (NRPB) publication. ISBN: 0/85951/3203.

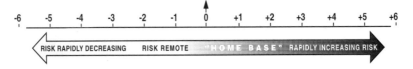

## Fig 7. - RISK OF BECOMING A CRIME STATISTIC

(1)• **Risk of being murdered with a firearm = 5.89 X 10⁻⁵**
Source: Uniform Crime Reports, 1990. "Crime in the United States - published by U.S. Department of Justice, FBI." (US Government Printing Office, DC 20402.)
Table 18, pgs. 12 and 162
"12,847 out of a population of 227,131,000" = 5.89 X 10⁻⁵.

(2)• **Risk of being murdered = 9.2 X 10⁻⁵**
Source: Uniform Crime Reports, 1990. "Crime in the United States - published by U.S. Department of Justice, FBI." (US Government Printing Office, DC 20402.)
Table 18, pg. 162
"20,930 out of a population of 227,131,000" = 9.2 X 10⁻⁵.

(3)• **Risk of woman suffering forcible rape = 8.34 X 10⁻⁴**
Source: Uniform Crime Reports, 1990. "Crime in the United States- published by U.S. Department of Justice, FBI." (US Government Printing Office, DC 20402.)
Table 18, pg. 162
"94,644 incidents in a population of 2.27 X 10⁸" = 4.17 X 10⁻⁴ per person. And since this is only for women and they represent only half the population: X 2 for women only = 8.34 X 10⁻⁴.

(4)• **Risk of being burglarized = 1.23 X 10⁻²**
Source: Uniform Crime Reports, 1990. "Crime in the United States- published by U.S. Department of Justice, FBI." (US Government Printing Office, DC 20402.)
Table 18, pg. 162
"2,793,447 out of a population of 227,131,000" = 1.23 X 10⁻².

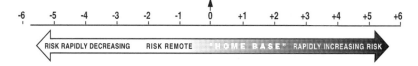

(5)• **Risk of incurring larceny/theft (including motor vehicles) = 3.8 X $10^{-2}$**
Source: Uniform Crime Reports, 1990. "Crime in the United States - published by U.S. Department of Justice, FBI." (US Government Printing Office, DC 20402.)
Table 18, pg. 162
"7,286,075 plus 1,515,364" = 8,801,439 out of a population of 227,131,000 = 3.8 X $10^{-2}$.

(6)• **Risk of your motor vehicle being stolen = 6.67 X $10^{-3}$**
Source: Uniform Crime Reports, 1990 "Crime in the United States published by U.S. Department of Justice, FBI." (US Government Printing Office, DC 20402.)
Table 18, pg. 162
"1,515,364 out of a population of 227,131,000" = 6.67 X $10^{-3}$.

(7)• **Risk of being murdered in Washington DC in 1992 = 7.6 X $10^{-4}$**
Source: Time Magazine, August 23, 1993, pg. 32, "Danger in the Safety Zone," Smolowe, J.
"76 in 100,000 = 7.6 X $10^{-4}$.

(8)• **Risk of being raped in Cleveland, Ohio 1992 = 1.6 X $10^{-3}$**
Source: Time Magazine, August 23, 1993, pg. 32, "Danger in the Safety Zone," Smolowe, J.
"166 per 100,000 = 1.6 X $10^{-3}$.

(9)• **Risk of being robbed in Newark, NJ in 1992 = 1.9 X $10^{-2}$**
Source: Time Magazine, August 23, 1993, pg. 32, "Danger in the Safety Zone," Smolowe, J.
"1,942 in 100,000= 1.9 X $10^{-2}$.

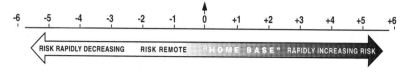

## Fig. 8 - THE PALING PERSPECTIVE SCALE<sup>SM</sup>

(1)• **Risk equivalent to one person in whole of U.S.A = 4 X 10⁻⁹**
*This represents a "-2¹/₂" on our scale.*
Source: The State of World Population, 1991, United Nations Population Fund, pg. 42, et seq.
"Total population of the U.S.A is 250 million" = 250 X 10⁶ = 2.5 X 10⁸.
Therefore one person in the population = 1/2.5 X 10⁸ = 4 X 10⁻⁹.

(2)• **Risk equivalent to one person in the whole world population = 1.8 X 10⁻¹⁰**
*This represents a "-3³/₄" on our scale.*
Source: The State of World Population, 1991, United Nations Population Fund, pg. 42, et seq.
"Total population of the planet is 5.6 (American) billion" = 5.6 X 10⁹.
Therefore one person in the population = 1/5.6 X 10⁹ = 0.18 X 10⁻⁹ = 1.8 X 10⁻¹⁰.

(3)• **This point represents what happens to half of the population.**
What people mean by "the average person" is the same as saying "what 50 percent of the people experience." This 50 percent level of risk is obviously the same as odds of 1 in 2, or 5 X 10⁻¹ to mathematical types and the point (3) shows where this fits on the scale.

NOTE: If the reader is surprised to see how near to the far right this point is, please look again at the way the top of the scale is marked. Because it is a logarithmic scale, each division is 10 times greater than the one before.

## Fig. 9 - RISKS FROM A U.S. LIFESTYLE

(1) • **Odds that a citizen will commit suicide with a firearm = 1 in 135 or 0.74 X $10^{-3}$**
Odds that an individual will die by committing suicide = 1 in 67 or 1.49 X $10^{-4}$ (Source: Les Krantz, <u>What the Odds Are</u>, 1992, pg. 257, HarperPerennial. ISBN: 0-06-271521)
But about half of all suicides are by firearms (Source: U.S. Department of Commerce, <u>Statistical Abstract of the United States 1993</u>, pg. 99, Chart 137, U.S. Government Printing Office. ISBN: 0-16-042046-6)
Thus 1 in 135 suicides involve firearms.

(2) • **Likelihood there is a gun in the home = 1 in 2 or 5 X $10^{-1}$**
"Guns are found in roughly half of America's households"
Source: <u>Economist,</u> March 26, 1994, pg. 15 (a very extensive article about guns in America)

(3) • **Annual death toll from alcohol abuse = 6 X $10^{-4}$**
Source: Harvard Center for Risk Analysis, <u>Annual Report,</u> 1991
Annual Death toll from alcohol abuse in U.S.A. = 150,000 people out or total population of 250,000,000 = 15 X $10^{4}$ / 2.5 X $10^{8}$ = 6 X $10^{-4}$
In addition to the direct results of alcohol use, there is strong evidence that alcohol is involved indirectly to a much larger number of society's problems and cost.

(4) • **Odds of an American having AIDS = 8 X $10^{-4}$**
Source: Les Krantz, <u>What the Odds Are</u>, 1992, pg. 11, HarperPerennial. ISBN: 0-06-271-521
Federal Center for Disease Control quotes "1 in about 250 Americans (a million) have been infected with the HIV virus, but only about 1 in 5 HIV carriers (200,000) have AIDS symptoms, which represents 1 in 1,250 Americans" = 8 X $10^{-4}$

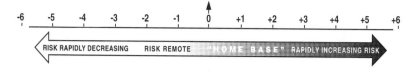

**THE PALING PERSPECTIVE SCALE**

RISK RAPIDLY DECREASING    RISK REMOTE    RAPIDLY INCREASING RISK

See also: U.S. Department of Commerce, <u>Statistical Abstract of the United States 1993</u>, pg. 96, Chart 131, U.S. Government Printing Office.

(5) • **Odds of a family living below the poverty line = 1.43 X 10⁻¹**

Source: Les Krantz, <u>What the Odds Are</u>, 1992, pg. 217, HarperPerennial. ISBN: 0-06-271-521

"There are 35.4 million poor in the U.S.A. out of a population of 250,000,000. Odds of 1 in 7 or 1.43 X 10⁻¹

See also: U.S. Department of Commerce, <u>Statistical Abstract of the United States 1993</u>, pg. 47, Chart 50, United States Printing Office.

(6) • **Odds that a student will drop out of school = 1 X 10⁻¹**

Source: Les Krantz, <u>What the Odds Are</u>, 1992, HarperPerennial. ISBN 0-06-271521

Dropouts from school are listed as students who leave before high school graduation = 1 in 10 for whole school population.

(7) • **Odds of a person under 18 years being arrested = 2.87 X 10⁻²**

Source: Les Krantz, <u>What the Odds Are</u>, 1992, pg. 58, HarperPerennial. ISBN: 0-06-271521

"One is 35 Americans under the age of 18 will be arrested" = 2.87 X 10⁻²

(8) • **Risk that a child will be criminally abused or neglected = 1 X 10⁻²**

Source: Les Krantz, <u>What the Odds Are</u>, 1992, pg. 56, HarperPerennial. ISBN: 0-06-571521

In the U.S. there are odds of 1 in 100 that a child will be criminally abused or neglected. (approximately 1 in 2,000 will die as a result.)

See also: U.S. Department of Commerce, <u>Statistical Abstract for United States 1993</u>, pg. 209, Chart 341, United States Printing Office.

THE PALING PERSPECTIVE SCALE

RISK RAPIDLY DECREASING   RISK REMOTE   RAPIDLY INCREASING RISK

(9) • **Odds of a prison inmate having been abused as a child = 8 X 10⁻¹**
Source: Les Krantz, <u>What the Odds Are</u>, 1992, pg. 8, HarperPerennial. ISBN: 0-06-571521
4 out of 5

(10) • **Odds of a child being born to a single black mother = 86 percent**
Source: U.S. Department of Commerce, <u>Statistical Abstract for the United States 1993</u>, pg. 77, Chart 98, United States Printing Office.

(11) • **Odds of a child being born to a single white mother = 30 percent**
Source: U.S. Department of Commerce, <u>Statistical Abstract for the United States 1993</u>, pg. 77, Chart 98, United States Printing Office.

(12) • **Risk of marriage ending in divorce = 4 X 10⁻¹**
Source; Les Krantz, <u>What the Odds Are</u>, 1992, pg. 83, HarperPerennial. ISBN: 0-06-571521
Odds of divorce in the U.S. are 2 out of 5 or 40 percent.
Source: U.S. Department of Commerce, <u>Statistical Abstract for the United States 1993</u>, pg. 101, Chart 144, United States Printing Office.

-6   -5   -4   -3   -2   -1 EFFECTIVE 0 ZERO   +1   +2   +3   +4   +5   +6

*A Special Invitation For You*

In our quest to continually improve scientifically based risk communication for the public, we invite you to send us your stories of your experiences, opinions and insights.

**Please send your comments to:**

Risk Communication & Environmental Institute, 5822 N.W. 91st Boulevard, Gainesville, Florida 32653

or

E-mail: jpaling@aol.com

# Want to know more
## about applying the wisdom
### in
# Up To Your Armpits in Alligators?

Additional learning materials are available to order on the next page. John Paling is also available to speak to your organization or to provide assistance in putting the Paling Perspective Scale^SM to work for you.

## REQUEST/ ORDER FORM

## LEARNING MATERIALS

❑ Please send me ____ copies of the book *"Up to Your Armpits in Alligators? - How to sort out what risks are worth worrying about!"* **$25.00\*each**

❑ Please send me ____ copies of the 3-tape audio series updating and expanding upon *"Up to Your Armpits in Alligators? - How to sort out what risks are worth worrying about!"* **$34.95\* per series**

❑ Please send me the 24-item set of 35mm color transparencies (with teaching notes) outlining the principles and uses of the The Paling Perspective Scale[SM] **$99.00\* per set**

## SPECIAL CUSTOMIZED SERVICES

❑ Assistance in researching or putting client figures on the The Paling Perspective Scale[SM]. Please inquire.

❑ Transparencies customized for client needs. Please inquire.

❑ **Please send me more information about booking Dr. John Paling to**
   • **speak to our conference or seminar**
   • **provide consulting services**
   • **organize a risk communication workshop**

*\*All orders include shipping and handling in Continental U.S.A. and a 30-day, money-back guarantee.*
*Please add 6% tax on orders from Florida*
*Quantity Discounts Available*

---

Name_____

Position _____

Company_____

Address _____

City _____ State_____ Zip_____

Phone (    )_____ FAX (    )_____

**Make Checks Payable to : John Paling & Co., Ltd**
5822 N.W. 91st Boulevard, Gainesville, Florida 32653
Phone (352) 377-2142 : FAX (352) 377-2351

*Take Care & Enjoy!*